Sophie Simon
Solves Them All

LISA GRAFF
PICTURES BY JASON BEENE

Sophie Simon
Solves Them All

SCHOLASTIC INC.

To Melissa, a bonafide smarty-pants

ISBN 978-0-545-52292-2

12 11 10 9 8 7 6 5 4 3 2 1   12 13 14 15 16 17/0

Printed in the U.S.A.   40

First Scholastic printing, September 2012

Designed by Jay Colvin

Contents

Who's Who

1. Sophie Simon: The smartest girl in the third grade (possibly the world)
2. Mr. and Mrs. Simon: Like to refer to their daughter as their "darling little sausage omelet"
3. Mr. St. Cupid: The dumbest teacher in all of Eisenberg Elementary (possibly the world)
4. Owen Luu: Likes things clean, quiet, and bland
5. Mrs. Luu: Likes things chaotic, loud, and spicy
6. Daisy Pete: Give her an inch, and she'll trip all over it
7. Mr. and Mrs. Pete: Own Petes' Pet Store. Want their daughter to be a star ballerina
8. Madame Robespierre: Teaches ballet with an iron fist
9. Julia McGreevy: Wants to be a famous journalist when she grows up. Wants to be a mathlete never
10. Professor McGreevy: Can't stop talking about math
11. Lenny the Lemur: A ring-tailed lemur

Sophie Simon
Solves Them All

A Genius with a Problem

Every morning as they walked to the bus stop, Sophie Simon and her parents had the same conversation.

"Have fun at school today, lamb chop," her mother would say, straightening out Sophie's blouse.

And Sophie would wrinkle her cute button nose at her mother and tell her, "School is not for fun. It's for learning."

But that Friday morning, instead of simply patting Sophie on the head and nodding, Sophie's parents did something that surprised her.

"Snickerdoodle," Sophie's father replied, "your

mother and I have been thinking. Perhaps today you might try to make some friends."

Sophie tugged at the straps of her backpack. "No, thank you," she said. "I don't need friends."

"But, walnut," Sophie's mother said, taking hold of her hand as they crossed the street. "Don't you even want one or two friends? All of the other children seem to have them."

"That's true," said Sophie's father.

Sophie scowled at her parents.

She was *not* like other children.

Sophie Simon was a *genius*.

By the time Sophie Simon was two, she could recite the alphabet backwards and forwards. The Russian alphabet.

By the time she was four, Sophie had dismantled her parents' broken toaster and turned it into a working radio.

And at the age of seven, Sophie had successfully performed open-heart surgery on an earthworm in the front yard.

Since earthworms have five hearts each, this was a pretty difficult task.

You would think that having a genius for a daughter would have made Sophie's parents delighted.

It did not.

Aileen and Maxwell Simon worried that their daughter wasn't "well-adjusted."

They were always quoting the famed child expert Doctor Wanda, who told parents on her TV show that the worst thing they could do was push their children to grow up too quickly.

To Sophie's parents, growing up too quickly meant doing anything Sophie found interesting.

If Sophie crafted a working robot out of

toothpicks and rubber bands, her parents sighed and told her that well-adjusted children made birdhouses.

If Sophie taught herself to speak Japanese from a textbook, her parents shook their heads and said that well-adjusted children spoke pig Latin.

And if Sophie composed her own concerto on the neighbor's grand piano, her parents rubbed their temples and complained that well-adjusted children played the kazoo.

Sometimes Sophie wondered if maybe her parents weren't really her parents. Maybe, Sophie thought, she had been switched with another baby in the hospital. A well-adjusted baby. Maybe her real parents were out in the world somewhere right now, wondering why their daughter wanted to play with dolls instead of encyclopedias.

But really, Sophie knew that the people who walked her to the bus stop every morning *were* her real parents. Because Sophie had her mother's wavy hair, blond like straw. And she had her father's blue eyes, and the same curvy earlobes. So she most definitely had not been switched at birth.

Too bad.

"Gumdrop," Sophie's father said as they reached the bus stop. They were the first ones there, as usual. "Isn't that nice boy from your class having a birthday party this Sunday?"

"Why, yes," Sophie's mother said. "That charming little boy we met at parents' night. Owen Luu. The one who was afraid of paste. He seemed *extremely* well-adjusted."

Sophie rolled her eyes.

If Owen Luu was well-adjusted, then she was the president of Finland.

"That's the one," Sophie's father said. "An invitation for the party came in the mail last week. Wouldn't you like to go, marshmallow? It's going to be a 'birthday pool-party extravaganza.' There will be an eight-layer ice cream cake, a high-dive contest, and an old-fashioned taffy pull."

"Oh, peanut, doesn't that sound delightful?" her mother exclaimed. "It would be a perfect opportunity to make friends."

Sophie didn't answer. She had never been to a birthday party, and she never wanted to go to one, either. And she certainly didn't want any *friends*. Sophie knew for a fact that she didn't need friends.

7

Friends did things like hang from the monkey bars and trade stickers.

Friends told each other secrets and laughed at silly jokes.

Having friends sounded like a waste of time.

"You know," Sophie said, trying to change the subject, "you really don't have to walk me to the bus stop anymore. I'm old enough to come by myself."

"Oh, bean sprout!" her mother said. "We could never let you walk all this way by yourself!"

"It's three whole blocks!" her father agreed. "What if you got lost?"

At dinner the night before, Sophie had built a topographic map of Zimbabwe out of her mashed potatoes. She would *not* have gotten lost.

"Here, dumpling," her mother said. "I made some cupcakes for your lunch. Let me put them in your backpack." She tugged at Sophie's zipper.

"Mom," Sophie said, "I've told you. I don't like cupcakes."

Sophie's favorite dessert was flan, a Mexican custard that her parents said looked like refrigerated cat food.

"Don't be silly, graham cracker!" her mother

said as she opened Sophie's backpack. "All well-adjusted children like cup—"

She did not finish her sentence.

"Sophie!" she screeched, her head halfway inside the backpack.

"What?" Sophie's father asked. "What is it?"

"Oh, Maxwell, you won't believe what I found in our daughter's bag! It's a . . ." She pulled out the object, and her husband snatched it from her.

"No!" he gasped.

"Yes!" Sophie's mother cried.

"It's a textbook!"

"A *college* textbook!"

"Mom," Sophie said. "Dad. I—" But she didn't get a chance to explain.

"Advanced Concepts in Modern Calculus," her father read. "Oh, Aileen, just imagine! Our well-adjusted daughter, exposed to this . . . *educational material*! The kind of stuff most *adults* don't understand!"

Sophie's mother put a hand on his shoulder. "Now, Maxwell, calm down. We don't even know if this book belongs to Sophie. Someone could have slipped it into her bag without her noticing. Let's give her a chance to explain before we get so worked up." She turned to Sophie. "Sugarplum?"

Sophie shrugged. "I just wanted to look at it on the bus," she said. "That's all."

Sophie's mother sucked in her breath. "Sophie!" she cried. "All this time you promised you'd only spend your free time reading comic books!"

"May I have my book back?" Sophie asked. "I want to study before school starts."

"Oh, Maxwell!" Sophie's mother wailed, grabbing her husband's arm. "Where did we go wrong?"

Sophie's father was shaking his head. "You try so hard to be a good parent," he said. "And then you find out your eight-year-old daughter is studying *calculus*."

Sophie puffed out her cheeks.

Other children were beginning to join them at the bus stop.

"But calculus is interesting," she tried to explain.

Sophie's father pointed an angry finger at her. "Don't you tell me calculus is interesting, young lady. I happen to know that calculus is *not* interesting. Calculus is *math*."

Sophie's father was right about one thing. Calculus *was* math. A very complicated kind of math. It involved long equations with letters and numbers and symbols so confusing that most people avoided looking at them directly, in case their brains turned to mush. There were graphs and charts and formulas and silly words like *tangent*.

Sophie loved it. She loved it more than any subject she'd ever studied before. Sophie loved calculus the way other children love roller coasters and trips to Disneyland.

She stayed up past midnight studying under the covers.

She thought about equations while her parents made her watch TV.

She even dreamed about calculus.

But there was one problem.

If Sophie *really* wanted to study calculus, really and truly, she needed a special kind of calculator.

"Mom? Dad?" Sophie asked as the Number 17 bus appeared over the hill in the distance. "Will you buy me a graphing calculator? I want the Pembo Q-60. It's the latest model. It costs one hundred dollars."

There was a pause.

A very short pause.

And in that pause, Sophie imagined what it might be like to have parents who understood her.

Parents who said, "Yes, dear, of *course* you may have a graphing calculator. Would you like a new set of notebooks and some fresh pencils to go along with it?"

Parents who let her study in peace and stopped bothering her about pointless things, like making friends.

But then the pause ended.

"Oh, Maxwell!" Sophie's mother sobbed. "What would Doctor Wanda say?"

Sophie's father shook his head. "You try so hard to be a good parent," he said with a sniffle. "And then your eight-year-old daughter tells you she wants a *calculator*."

Sophie heaved a deep sigh.

"So you won't buy me a Pembo Q-60 then?" she asked.

"No," said her mother.

"Absolutely not," said her father.

The bus slowed to a stop at the corner.

"May I at least have my book back?" Sophie wondered.

"No," said her mother.

"Absolutely not," said her father.

"But it's from the library!" Sophie protested. "I have to return it."

"Oh, Maxwell!" Sophie's mother wailed. "Our little girl's been visiting the *library*!"

Sophie's father shook his head. "You try so hard to be a good parent . . ." he began.

But Sophie didn't hear the rest. The second the bus doors squeaked open, she leaped up the steps and plopped herself into the first empty seat.

As the bus pulled away from the corner, Sophie watched her parents' faces grow smaller and smaller, weeping as they clutched her calculus book. When they had finally become specks in the distance and then disappeared, she turned around and thought.

There had to be *some* way to get that calculator. But how?

Sophie Simon didn't know it, but at that very moment, there were three other third-graders on the Number 17 bus who were puzzling over problems of their own.

Doozies.

Dilemmas.

Submarine-size pickles.

It would have taken a *genius* to solve all four problems.

Too bad Sophie Simon only cared about one of them.

Check Marks and Squeegees

Daisy Pete sat at her desk in Mr. St. Cupid's third-grade class, tapping her pencil and staring at the list of rules on the wall.

There were lots of rules in Mr. St. Cupid's class.

There were normal ones.

No pushing
No hitting
No chewing gum

And strange ones.

No choking
No wearing orange socks
No talking about fungus

Whenever anybody did something Mr. St. Cupid didn't like, the teacher would add a new rule to his list.

So far the list of rules covered nineteen sheets of poster board and spread across three walls.

As Daisy stared at the list, the pencil she was tapping on her desk flew out of her hand and straight up into the air.

It landed—*ker-PLUNK!*—on the head of the girl who sat in front of her.

Sophie Simon.

Sophie was so busy reading the book she had hidden under her desk, she didn't even notice the pencil sticking out of her blond ponytail.

Daisy thought Sophie Simon was a little odd. All she ever did was read. And trying to talk to her was like riding a bicycle upside down.

It didn't make any sense.

No wonder Sophie Simon didn't have any friends.

Daisy leaned forward and plucked her pencil

out of Sophie's hair. Luckily, Mr. St. Cupid didn't notice. If he had, she would have gotten in trouble for breaking Rule number 138:

No pulling objects out of other students' heads

Daisy did not want to get in trouble.

Every time you broke a rule in Mr. St. Cupid's class, you got a check mark next to your name on the board.

If you got three check marks, you had to stay inside for final recess and clean the windows.

Daisy hadn't been outside for final recess once all year.

Daisy never broke rules on purpose. But she seemed to be especially good at getting into trouble in Mr. St. Cupid's class.

In fact, Daisy was responsible for creating thirty-six of the rules on Mr. St. Cupid's wall, including:

No spilling glitter on the rug
No falling over in your desk
No dropping your science book on your foot
No tripping over your science book

No tripping over your backpack
No tripping over your shoelaces
NO TRIPPING

Daisy Pete had a lot of problems when it came to tripping.

But somehow, that Friday afternoon, Daisy only had two check marks next to her name. If she could make it through the rest of math time without breaking any more rules, she would finally get to go outside for final recess.

Daisy wondered what it was like out there. She'd heard rumors there were ice cream sundaes and dodgeball.

She was pretty sure the dodgeball part was true, at least.

"If I had *five* onions," Mr. St. Cupid bellowed at the class, "and I ate *three*, what would I be *left* with?"

No one raised a hand.

No one ever raised a hand in Mr. St. Cupid's class.

Daisy thought this was because Rule number 3 on the wall was

No moving your arms

Most days, Daisy thought Mr. St. Cupid's rules were pretty stupid. But today, having rules didn't seem like such a bad idea. Daisy could think of some good ones for her parents.

No yelling
No lecturing

And, most important,

No forcing your daughter to dance in a ballet recital

Daisy had been trying to get out of her ballet recital for weeks.

She told her parents that she hated ballet, and that her dance teacher was meaner than an angry werewolf.

She told them that the thought of falling over in front of hundreds of people at a dance recital made her want to spew her lunch all over her frilly pink tutu.

She told them that if they forced her to dance in the recital at the Middlebury Performing Arts Center on Saturday, it would be *utterly unfair*.

But did Daisy's parents pay any attention when she told them those things?

They did not.

Daisy's parents told her that she probably just had stage fright.

They told her that, when she got up onstage, she'd be a star.

They told her that, once she was a star, the world would be her oyster, and she wouldn't be stuck working in a pet store all her life like they were.

Well, Daisy didn't want any oysters. And she loved Petes' Pet Store. She couldn't imagine anything better than working there forever.

But when it came to ballet class, Daisy's parents didn't hear a single thing she said. It made Daisy feel *absolutely powerless*.

Sometimes Daisy wondered if maybe her parents weren't really her parents. Maybe, Daisy thought, her real parents had been abducted by aliens just after she was born, and replaced with androids who didn't understand that going to ballet class was worse than having your nose hairs yanked out with pliers. Maybe her real parents were up in a spaceship right now, watching their daughter as they orbited the earth, cringing every time she had to put on a leotard.

But really, Daisy knew that the people who bought her dance shoes and picked her up from class every Tuesday after school *were* her real parents. Because Daisy had seen lots of movies about aliens, and her parents didn't do anything weird and alieny like drink mountains of sugar water or shoot lasers out of their eyeballs. So they most definitely had not been abducted.

Too bad.

Daisy was snapped out of her thoughts by something poking into her left elbow. She turned to look.

At the desk next to her, Julia McGreevy was holding a folded-up square of paper.

"For Owen," Julia whispered.

Julia McGreevy and Owen Luu were best friends. Julia sat at the desk to Daisy's left, and Owen sat at the desk to Daisy's right.

Daisy passed a lot of notes.

Today, though, Daisy thought about ignoring Julia. Note passing was against the rules. If Daisy got caught, it would mean no final recess for sure.

"Please?" Julia begged.

Daisy sighed and took the note.

But just as she was about to place it on Owen's desk, Daisy sneezed.

When Daisy sneezed, she dropped things.

Daisy dropped the note.

Owen stuck his leg out to the side like a stretched-out dish towel, trying to cover up the note. But it was too late.

"*Mister* Luu!" Mr. St. Cupid shouted. "*What* are you doing?"

"I-I'm not d-doing anything," Owen stuttered.

"*Stop stuttering!*" yelled Mr. St. Cupid. "Stuttering is not allowed in my class! New rule!"

Daisy gulped.

Mr. St. Cupid walked over to Owen's desk and glared down at him. "*Why* is your *leg* stuck out like that?"

"Um . . ." Owen said. "I'm, um, stretching?"

"Well, it's *distracting!*" Mr. St. Cupid bellowed. "From now on, *stretching* is not allowed in my class! *New rule!*"

Daisy grimaced.

"But I had a leg cramp," Owen said.

"*Leg cramps* aren't allowed in my class, *either*! That's *three* checks for you, Mr. Luu! No final recess!"

22

Daisy gargled.

"O-okay," Owen said. He slowly brought his leg back under his desk, pressing the note down hard into the carpet.

"Now," Mr. St. Cupid said. He returned to the front of the classroom. "If I had *five* onions, and I ate *three*, what would— *Mister* Luu!" He pointed to Owen's foot. "Is that a *note*?"

Daisy sucked in all her breath and puffed out her cheeks.

Owen's face was red as a rib of rhubarb. "M-maybe?" he said.

"Hand it over!"

Daisy crossed her fingers.

Owen scooped the note off the floor. "I didn't, um, write it," he said as he gave it to the teacher.

Daisy crossed her toes.

"I d-don't even know what it, um, says."

Daisy crossed her eyes.

"Well," Mr. St. Cupid said, "why don't we all find out *together* then?" And he unfolded the paper and began to read aloud.

If Mr. St. Upid ate three onions, he'd be left with stinky breath.

"Class!" Mr. St. Cupid hollered. "Whoever wrote this *note* has broken a very serious *rule*."

Daisy's eyeballs were bulging from holding her breath too long.

"My *name*," Mr. St. Cupid said, "is spelled like *this*."

He wrote it on the board.

MR. ST. CUPID

"It has a *C* in it, class. St. *Cupid*. Not St. *Upid*." He wrote that on the board, too.

MR. ST. UPID

"I simply *cannot* understand why my students continue to spell my name incorrectly *every* year. *Rule number thirty-nine!*" He pointed to the list:

No spelling anything rong

"*Now!*" Mr. St. Cupid shouted. "Let us *return* to *math*!"

Daisy returned to breathing.

"If I had *five*—"

Mr. St. Cupid stopped talking again as he passed in front of Daisy's row. "*What* are you doing?" he bellowed.

He was looking directly at Daisy.

Daisy knocked three erasers out of her desk, which was against Rule number 77:

No dropping three things at once

But Mr. St. Cupid didn't notice.

"*Miss* Simon!" he hollered.

He wasn't hollering at Daisy.

He was hollering at Sophie Simon.

The teacher strode over to Sophie's desk. "*Miss* Simon!" he shouted, spitting a little on the *s*'s. "Are you reading a *book* under your *desk* during *math* time?"

Sophie Simon always read books under her desk during math time. Daisy had been watching her do it all year. Sophie read books under her desk during science time, too. And during language arts time, and social studies time, and music time.

During silent reading time, she worked on chemistry experiments.

Sophie placed a finger in her book and looked up at Mr. St. Cupid. She showed him what she was reading.

"*Principles of Civil Disobedience,*" he read.

"Yes," Sophie said. "It's all about how, throughout history, people who were *absolutely powerless*"—Daisy's ears perked up—"fought against authority by refusing to follow laws or rules they felt were *utterly unfair.*" Daisy sat up a little straighter in her desk. "Like in India in 1930," Sophie went on, "when the government made buying salt illegal so a man named Gandhi led a march to the seashore to collect it. And in North Carolina in 1960, when African-Americans weren't served at lunch counters because of their race, so they staged protests called 'sit-ins.' Or nowadays, when parents won't buy their children graphing calculators, so the kids have to figure out how—"

Mr. St. Cupid slapped a hand on Sophie's desk.

"Rule number sixty!" he shouted, pointing to the wall.

No reading books fatter than your head

"You will learn about *history* in *high* school!" Mr. St. Cupid bellowed at Sophie, plucking the book from her hands. *"Third* grade is for learning *subtraction* and tying your *shoes!"*

"But I already know those things," Sophie said with a sigh.

"Rule number forty-five!" Mr. St. Cupid screeched at her. He pointed.

No sighing

"*Three checks!* No final recess for *you*, Miss Simon!"

And he tossed Sophie's book in the garbage can.

As Mr. St. Cupid went back to hollering about onions, Daisy sat at her desk and thought.

Was it really true that powerless people could find a way to change their lives, like Sophie had said? Just by refusing to do something they didn't think was fair?

Was all of that in the book Sophie had been reading?

Daisy stared at the garbage can.

Maybe, she thought, there was some hope for her after all.

"*Miss Pete!*"

Daisy looked up to see Mr. St. Cupid glaring down at her. His cheeks were puffed out like tomatoes.

"Why aren't you paying *attention*?"

Daisy blinked. "I was just . . ." she said, "thinking."

"*Unacceptable!*" Mr. St. Cupid shouted. "New rule!"

And he walked over to his list of rules and added a new one.

Then he put a third check mark by Daisy's name.

While everyone else was outside for final recess, Daisy and Owen were cleaning windows with squeegees.

Sophie was not cleaning windows with a squeegee.

She was reading her book from the garbage can.

"Sophie?" Daisy said.

Sophie did not look up.

Daisy tried again. "Can you help me with something?"

"No, thank you," Sophie said, turning a page. "I'd rather not."

Daisy looked over at Owen, but he was busy squeegeeing his window.

"I need your help," Daisy told Sophie. "I need you to teach me about that civil disinfectant stuff."

"Civil disobedience?" Sophie said.

"Yeah." Daisy nodded. "I need to learn how to get out of my ballet recital tomorrow. Does it say anything about that in there?" She pointed to the book.

"No," Sophie said.

She turned another page.

"Look," Daisy told her, waving her squeegee in the air. "Haven't you ever had a problem of your own?"

A blob of water flew off the squeegee and landed—*PLOP!*—at Sophie's feet.

Sophie kept reading.

"A really really *big* problem?" Daisy went on.

Another two blobs flew off the squeegee and landed—*PLOP! PLOP!*—on Sophie's head.

Sophie still kept reading.

"A problem so huge," Daisy said, "that you thought there'd never be any way to solve it?"

Three more blobs landed—*PLOP! PLOP! PLOP!*—right in the middle of Sophie's book.

Sophie Simon finally raised her head.

"I want a calculator," she said. "A Pembo Q-60. It's the very latest model. It costs one hundred dollars."

Daisy thought that one hundred dollars sounded like an awful lot of money for a calculator. But she didn't say that.

"I can help you get it," she said instead. "If you get me out of my ballet recital."

Sophie raised her eyebrows. "Do you have one hundred dollars?"

"No," Daisy said. "I only have"—she added up all her saved allowance—"five. But I bet the other girls in my ballet class would chip in, too. *No one* wants to dance in the recital tomorrow. There are thirteen of us, and we could each give you five dollars. That's enough, right?"

Sophie frowned at Daisy.

"If thirteen ballerinas each gave me five dollars," she said, "I'd only have sixty-five."

Daisy scratched her cheek. "So that's not enough then?" she asked.

"I'd still need thirty-five more dollars for my calculator."

From the window, Owen hiccuped.

"But you could help me anyway," Daisy told her.

The bell rang for the end of final recess. Owen crossed the room to put away his squeegee.

"I don't see why I should help you get out of your recital," Sophie said, "if you can't help me get a calculator."

"But—"

"Anyway," Sophie went on, "the principles of civil disobedience would never work in your case. You'd need someone from the newspaper to cover the story, and we couldn't find anyone on such short notice."

"The newspaper?" Daisy asked.

She didn't know anyone who worked for a newspaper.

Sophie shrugged. "Sorry."

And with that, she walked over to Mr. St. Cupid's desk, tucked her book back in the garbage can under a slimy banana peel, and sat down at her desk.

Daisy sighed and walked to the suds bucket to put her squeegee back.

She slipped—*SWISH!*

And tripped—*CLUNK!*

And crashed—*THUD!*

"Rule number twenty-nine!" Mr. St. Cupid hollered as he entered the room. *"No falling on your butt in the squeegee water!"*

This, Daisy thought as she lay on her rear end in the middle of the classroom, was exactly why she needed to get out of that recital tomorrow.

But if Sophie wouldn't help her, what could she do?

Piranhas and Pet Stores

Every afternoon, on the Number 17 bus coming home from school, Owen Luu sat in the exact same seat.

The second seat from the front, on the right side.

He always sat there with his best friend, Julia McGreevy. Julia didn't care which seat she sat in, but it was very important to Owen.

The second seat on the right was the cleanest one on the whole bus.

It didn't have dirt smears on the seat.

It didn't have stuffing coming out of the bench.

It didn't have gum underneath that your leg might stick to.

Owen hated dirty bus seats. They were grimy and messy and gross. Owen didn't like being grimy and messy and gross. He was happiest when his clothes were ironed, his ears were washed, and his shoelaces were double-knotted.

But on Friday afternoon, as the bus pulled away from Eisenberg Elementary, Owen wasn't sitting in his usual seat with Julia.

He was sitting in the fourth seat from the back on the left side, which was the second to grossest seat on the whole bus.

And he was sitting next to Sophie Simon.

Owen was sitting there because he had a problem.

A huge problem.

An *enormous* problem.

And he was positive that Sophie Simon was the only person who could help him.

But Sophie wasn't paying any attention to him. Owen didn't even think she knew he was there. She was busy reading a gigantic book called *Basics of Human Psychology*.

Owen didn't know how Sophie could read a

book like that. He got bored halfway through the title.

Sophie sure was weird, he thought. She was always reading boring books. And talking to Sophie made his brain dizzier than a windup monkey toy.

No wonder she didn't have any friends.

Owen looked to the front of the bus. He half-hoped Julia would be looking his way so he could make "I really can't do this" eyes at her, and she'd understand and make "It's okay, come sit up here with me" eyes at him.

Julia wasn't looking his way.

She was holding a piece of paper over her head. She'd ripped one out of her green journalist's notebook and scribbled a note on it. Owen knew she'd written it just for him.

Get on with it already.

Owen ran his hands over the creases in his pants.

He turned back to Sophie Simon.

"Um, Sophie?" he said softly.

Sophie did not look up.

Owen cleared his throat and tried again.

"Um? *Sophie?*"

She still did not look up.

Maybe it was useless, Owen thought. His problem was too big. Probably even someone as smart as Sophie Simon couldn't solve a problem as big as his.

It all had to do with his birthday on Sunday.

For most kids, birthdays were happy times.

For most kids, birthdays meant pin the tail on the donkey and balloons and maybe a dinosaur cake.

Most kids did not have Owen's mother.

This year, Owen's mother was planning a "birthday pool-party extravaganza."

There would be an eight-layer ice cream cake.

There would be a high-dive contest.

And there would be an "old-fashioned taffy pull."

Owen didn't like eight-layer ice cream cakes. One of the layers always toppled off your plate and landed in your lap and got you messy.

He didn't like high-dive contests. He was terrified of heights and petrified of diving.

And he did *not* want to participate in an old-fashioned taffy pull. Taffy was sticky and sloppy and sweet. He didn't want to pull it. He didn't want to do *anything* to it.

But the worst part of Owen's birthday was the present.

Every year, Owen asked his mom for something he really, really wanted.

And every year, she got him something completely different.

Two years ago, when Owen was turning seven,

he'd asked his mom for a new pair of shoes—black lace-up ones to go with his school pants. Owen had really wanted a pair of nice, clean, shiny black school shoes.

But Mrs. Luu hadn't gotten him nice, clean, shiny black school shoes.

Instead, she'd bought him antigravity boots.

Those boots sent Owen flying into the ceiling like a rocket, and off to the hospital with a concussion.

Last year, for Owen's eighth birthday, he'd asked for a book about robots—one with colorful pictures and fun facts about robots through the ages. Owen had really wanted a nice, small, fact-filled book about robots.

But Mrs. Luu hadn't gotten him a nice, small, fact-filled book about robots.

Instead, she'd bought him an actual, life-size robot with "realistic battle action noises" and a toy laser gun.

That robot had fired sparks at Owen for five days straight, until he finally figured out how to take out the batteries.

It seemed like no matter what Owen wanted, his mother got him the *exact opposite*.

So *this* year, Owen hadn't been so sure it was a good idea to tell his mother what he wanted. But she'd promised to get him exactly what he asked for.

Crossed her heart and everything.

So Owen told her.

He said that all he wanted in the world—the only thing he'd wanted for *years*, actually—was a rabbit. A nice, gentle, soft, quiet little rabbit of his very own.

And when Owen's mom had replied, "Oh, a pet is a *fabulous* idea!" well, for a second there, Owen had thought he might actually get a birthday present he wanted for a change.

But fifteen minutes later, Owen overheard his mom on the phone with Petes' Pet Store, asking Mr. and Mrs. Pete if they had any "really exotic" pets she could buy for her son's birthday.

"Do you have any alligators or duck-billed platypuses?" she asked them. "Or maybe an aquarium full of piranhas? Owen would love that!"

Owen would *not* love an aquarium full of piranhas.

He wanted a rabbit.

But no matter how many times he told his mother that, he simply couldn't *convince* her.

She had already paid Mr. and Mrs. Pete a one-hundred-dollar deposit to find something "absolutely wild." And his birthday was in just two days. If he didn't do something quick, he'd never get a rabbit.

Sometimes Owen wondered if maybe his mother wasn't really his mother. Maybe, Owen thought, the person he *believed* was his mother was really his mom's evil twin, Esmeralda, a crazy woman who loved all the things Owen hated, like fireworks and roller coasters and jalapeño peppers. Maybe his real mother—who was much quieter and calmer and who would *never* buy him a piranha—was locked up in a cabin somewhere right now, far off in the woods, looking for a way out so she could give Owen a rabbit for his birthday.

But really, Owen knew that the woman who woke him up every morning by blaring mariachi music from the stereo *was* his real mother. Because Owen had asked his grandparents once, and they swore up and down there was no evil twin named Esmeralda. So Owen's mom was definitely not locked up in a far-off cabin.

Too bad.

But if anyone could think of a way to get his

mother to give him a rabbit, it was Sophie Simon.
She was the smartest girl in the third grade, possibly the world.

All Owen had to do was ask her.

"UM, SOPHIE?"

Sophie finally looked up from her book.

"Yes?" she said.

Owen blinked. Sophie Simon made him nervous. Most things made Owen nervous—clowns and geese and moving sidewalks and Mr. St. Cupid, just to name a few. But Sophie Simon made Owen *very* nervous. He felt like she could rearrange his brain cells just by looking at him.

"Um," he said again. "Could you, um, help me with something?"

"Probably," she said. "But I'd rather not."

And she went back to reading.

"Oh."

If Sophie didn't want to help him, what was Owen supposed to do?

Owen looked toward the front of the bus again.

Julia was holding up another piece of paper.

JUST ASK HER, YOU BABY!

"Um, Sophie?" Owen said, trying to be brave. "I need your help. I want a rabbit for my birthday, but my mom wants to get me a piranha or something. She already ordered a pet from Daisy Pete's parents' store, but I don't know what it is yet. Something terrible." He bit his lip. "I really think you should help me."

Sophie turned a page. "And why should I do that?" she asked.

"Well . . ." Owen thought hard. "During final recess today you told Daisy you wanted to buy a computer."

"A calculator," Sophie corrected him. "The Pembo Q-60. The latest model."

"Right," Owen said. "And you said you'd help Daisy with her problem if she could pay you enough money."

"But she couldn't," Sophie said. "She was short thirty-five dollars."

Owen didn't see what being short had to do with anything. But he said, "Well, if you helped me, I'd give you all my birthday money from Grandpa Ricky."

Sophie looked up.

"Twenty dollars," Owen told her.

Sophie looked back down.

"That still wouldn't be enough for the calculator," she said. "Even if I helped both of you. Which is a lot of helping. I'd still need fifteen dollars."

"But—"

"What makes you think I'd be able to help you anyway?" Sophie asked him.

"Oh, I'm sure it wouldn't be too tough for someone like you to figure out!" Owen said. "You know everything. You're always reading those big, fat books."

Owen looked at the page Sophie was reading.

"Reverse Psychology," it said at the top.

"What's reverse psychology?" he asked Sophie.

Sophie stuck a finger in her book to hold her place. "It's a way to *convince* someone of one thing"—Owen's ears perked up—"by telling them you want the *exact opposite*." Owen sat up a little straighter in his seat. "Like if a teacher wanted her students to do their spelling homework, so she told them that she didn't think they could do it because they weren't smart enough. Then they would try very hard and finish their homework, just to prove her wrong. Which was exactly what she wanted in the first place."

Owen thought about that.

"Does it work on moms?" he asked.

"What?" Sophie said.

"All that stuff you just said. Reverse photography."

"Reverse psychology," Sophie corrected.

"Yeah, that one."

The bus screeched to a stop.

"Stanford Avenue!" the bus driver called out.

"Sorry," Sophie said, zipping her book into her backpack. "This is my stop."

"But—"

"I have to get off," Sophie said. She poked him in the knee. "Please move."

"But I need your help!"

Sophie sighed. "Why don't you get your friend to help you?" she asked. "That curly-haired girl. Maybe she has some ideas."

The bus doors squeaked open.

The driver went outside to direct traffic.

"Julia won't help me," Owen said as Sophie squeezed past him into the aisle. "She's too busy trying to think of a story to write for the school newspaper."

"Newspaper?"

Sophie sat down so quickly that she landed right on top of Owen.

She didn't move.

She just stared at the top of Owen's head.

"Um, Sophie?" he said. She was acting sort of weird.

Plus she was wrinkling his pants.

"Sophie?" Owen said again.

Sophie blinked at him. "Did you say that Julia is looking for a news story?"

"Yeah," Owen said. "For the school paper. But she only has until Monday, and she'll never find one. Plus she doesn't have anything to type on. Last weekend her dad made her sell her typewriter at their yard sale. She got fifteen bucks for it."

Sophie's eyes grew wide as watermelons.

"Fifteen dollars?" she asked.

"Yeah," Owen said. "Why?"

The bus driver popped his head back inside the bus.

"Anyone else for Stanford Avenue?" he shouted.

Sophie grabbed Owen's hand.

"Come on!" she hollered.

She dragged him down the bus aisle.

"But-but . . ." Owen stuttered. "Where are we going? This isn't my stop. What if I—?"

One step from the bottom, Sophie whirled around to face him. "Do you want a rabbit?" she asked him. "Or do you want a piranha?"

And she leaped down the last step to Stanford Avenue.

Owen turned to look at Julia.

She was grinning at him.

"Well?" she said. "What are you waiting for?"

And just like that, right as the doors were about to close, Owen Luu made a decision.

"Sophie, wait!" he called, throwing himself from the bus just as the doors snapped shut behind him. "Wait, Sophie, wait! I DON'T WANT A PIRANHA!"

They'd been walking for about five minutes when suddenly Sophie stopped.

"Here we are!" she cried.

They were standing in front of Petes' Pet Store.

"Wh-what are we doing here?" Owen asked. Pet stores made him nervous. They were filled with guppies and geckos and gerbils.

"You said your mom is buying your birthday present from this pet store, right?"

"R-right," Owen said.

He peeked through the window.

Daisy Pete was in there, practicing her twirling.

She was not a very good twirler.

She twirled once.

She twirled twice.

She twirled three ti—

CRASH!

Daisy fell over.

From somewhere inside the store, a parrot squawked.

"If you want to use reverse psychology on your mother"—Sophie scanned the flyers pasted in the window—"and what you really want for your birthday is a rabbit"—she ran her finger down an advertisement for pet food—"then we need to make sure that the Petes sell your mom the exact *opposite* of a rabbit."

"Okay," Owen said. "But what's the exact opposite of a rabbit?"

"Well," Sophie said. She began to read a new flyer. "Would you say that a rabbit has long ears?"

Owen stuck his hands in his pockets. "Of course," he said.

"And would you say that it has a short, fluffy tail?"

"Very short," Owen told her. "And fluffy."

"And would you also say," Sophie went on, running her finger over the last row of flyers, "that a rabbit is very, very quiet?"

Owen nodded. "So the opposite of a rabbit," he said, beginning to understand, "would have short ears, a long tail, and be very, very loud?"

Sophie didn't answer him.

Instead, she slapped her hand over a flyer in the window.

"Perfect!" she cried out.

Owen squinted at the flyer.

When he turned back to talk to Sophie, she was inside the pet store.

Owen stood outside, staring at the flyer in the window. And he was still standing there two minutes later when Sophie popped her blond head out the door.

"Owen, come on!" she called to him. "Come on in here! We need to talk to Daisy. Oh, and you can get a letter to Julia for me, right?"

"Huh?"

But Sophie had disappeared inside the store again.

Owen gulped as he opened the door to the pet store.

Sophie Simon *and* pets?

What had he gotten himself into?

Very Ugly Hats

Julia McGreevy parked her bike in front of the Middlebury Performing Arts Center and looked up at the marquee.

Madame Robespierre
In Association with Eisenberg Elementary
Presents:
OOH LA LA
A ballet recital about the history of France

Blech, Julia thought.
Julia did not like ballet recitals.

She thought they were boring.

And long.

And pink.

But last night Julia had found a note slipped under her front door, a note that made her want to come to this particular ballet recital very badly.

Julia,

Looking for a big scoop?

Middlebury P.A.C. 2:00 p.m. tomorrow.

Bring fifteen dollars and your camera. Come in the rear entrance, and don't let anyone see you.

You won't be disappointed.

—Sophie Simon

P.S. Owen says hi.

Julia pulled her camera out of her bike basket and hung it around her neck.

She patted the folded bills in her pocket.

She checked her watch.

1:52.

Right on time.

Julia slipped inside the back door, which was propped open with a brick.

Julia sneaked past the dressing rooms, where

girls were busy getting ready. She didn't see Sophie Simon anywhere. How was Julia supposed to figure out what the big news story was if Sophie wasn't there to tell her? What a weirdo. All that girl ever did was read about boring stuff like history. And talking to her always made Julia feel like she was in the middle of a one-kid brain tornado.

No wonder she didn't have any friends.

Still, if Sophie could find Julia a big news story, it was definitely worth paying her fifteen dollars.

Julia really, really needed a big news story.

Every Monday, Julia turned in a story for the weekly paper. Stories about the mysterious meat loaf in the cafeteria, or the contaminated candy machine outside the teachers' lounge.

They were pretty good stories.

But every Tuesday, Miss Harbinger told Julia that she didn't print anyone's stories unless they were in fifth grade or higher.

That was *the Rule*.

But what Miss Harbinger didn't know was that, if Julia didn't publish a story in next week's paper, her dad was going to make her drop out of the journalism club.

And then, whether Julia liked it or not—and

Julia did *not*—her dad was going to make her sign up for the Math Olympics team.

As a mathlete.

Julia was not a mathlete. She was a journalist.

She just had to get a story published to prove it.

A man burst into the hallway. He was dressed all in black and had a headset stuck over his ears. "Five minutes to curtain!" he hollered.

He ignored Julia as he rushed past.

"Everybody to the stage!"

Well, Julia thought, if everyone else was going to the stage, she should, too. That was what a good journalist would do.

Julia ducked through the stage door and hid under a prop table on the side of the stage.

No one noticed her.

It was dark. The stage lights were off and the curtain was closed. Julia could hear murmurs from the audience on the other side.

It sounded like a big crowd.

Julia took her pencil from behind her ear and scribbled a note in the notebook she always kept in her back pocket.

PACKED AT THE P.A.C.

Julia always took lots of notes when she was working on a story. A reporter couldn't risk forgetting anything. It was just being smart.

Her father wouldn't think it was smart.

Professor McGreevy thought that there wasn't anything *smart* about working on a school newspaper.

The only thing Julia's dad thought about, all day every day, was math.

Math, math, math, math, math.

He quizzed Julia on her times tables over her morning cornflakes.

He picked her up early from birthday parties to talk about long division.

He even tucked her into bed with stories about Isaac Newton.

Ever since the day she was born, Professor McGreevy had been trying to make Julia as nuts about math as he was.

It was not going to work.

Julia McGreevy hated math worse than she hated the color pink.

Sometimes Julia wondered if maybe her father wasn't really her father. Maybe, Julia thought, sometime just after she was born, her dad had been hit over the head with a very large abacus, and it had shaken up his brain so much that he'd gotten amnesia. Maybe he'd forgotten all the things he *used* to like—normal dad things like golfing and barbecues, and reading bedtime stories like *The Tale of Peter Rabbit*—and now all he could remember were math problems. Maybe, Julia thought, if she just whacked her father hard enough in the right spot, he'd go back to being the nice, normal, non-mathy dad he was before.

But really, Julia knew that her father had always been the same math nerd he was today. Because sometimes he'd say things like "Back when I was your age, my team had won the regional Math Olympics three times already," and she'd seen the photos, too. So there most definitely was no need to whack her father over the head with something heavy.

Too bad.

Behind her, Julia heard a group coming through the stage door. She poked her head out from under the table to watch and listen.

One by one, the ballerinas filed past Julia's hiding spot and lined up on the stage. From underneath the table, Julia couldn't see any of the girls' heads— just their pink tutus and pink ballet slippers.

They were followed by a tall, thin woman holding a large wooden stick.

That must be Madame Robespierre.

Pound!

Madame Robespierre banged her stick on the ground as the last ballerina lined up onstage.

Julia counted them.

Thirteen.

Thirteen tiny, terrified tots in tutus.

Pound!

"Lay-DEEZ!" Madame Robespierre hollered at them.

She had a thick French accent, with vowels as sharp as her pointy shoes.

"Tonight you are telling zee 'istory of France!"

Pound!

"Zee story of my country!"

Pound!

"So you will wear zee 'atts proud-lee and zere will be no complaining!"

Pound!

Julia pulled her pencil out from behind her ear and scribbled in her notebook.

ATTS? she wrote. What was an att?

Julia inched out of her hiding spot to see.

She sucked in a breath when she saw what the girls had on their heads.

She had never seen anything so ugly.

HATS, Julia wrote in her notebook. *VERY UGLY HATS.*

Each one of the very ugly hats, which were also very large, was shaped like a different object, and

Julia guessed that they must all have something to do with France.

One girl was balancing an enormous wedge of stinky cheese, while another girl was teetering underneath a hat shaped like a huge bottle of perfume. A brown-haired girl across the stage was strapped to what appeared to be a two-ton plate of frogs' legs.

But the biggest and ugliest hat of all was Daisy Pete's. It was a gigantic sculpture, at least two feet high, that Julia recognized as an exact replica of the Eiffel Tower.

Julia thought that if she had to wear a humongous hat like that, she would topple over in a millisecond.

Was *this* why Sophie had told her to come today? Julia wondered. To see the giant ugly hats?

Pound!

Madame Robespierre slammed her stick on the ground again.

Pound!

"Zere will be absolutely no steenk-ing tonight," she hollered. "Do we all understand zat?"

Madame looked down her nose at each girl in turn.

Pound!

"Because sometimes you all steenk quite bad-lee!"

Julia wrote a new note in her book.

MRS. R. = NOT NICE

Pound!

Daisy Pete raised a hand.

Pound!

"What eez it, you stu-peed girl?" Madame asked.

In her notebook, Julia crossed out *NOT NICE* and wrote *MEAN*.

"Um, well," Daisy said. "I was just wondering, um, what if I *do* fall over? What if I . . . lose my balance?"

The other girls gasped.

Julia leaned forward until her neck was stretched like a rubber band.

Madame Robespierre did not pound her stick.

She didn't shout.

She didn't do any of the things that Julia thought she might.

Instead, she straightened her back and looked down at Daisy with a calm smile.

"It is very important to have zee balance," she said.

Daisy nodded.

"But zee problem," Madame said, "it is zee little baby toes."

She scratched her chin.

"Zey are no good for zee balance."

Madame Robespierre leaned down close, until her nose was just an inch away from Daisy's.

Daisy was shaking. The tower on her head looked like it was in the middle of an earthquake.

"So," Madame continued, "zee ballerinas in Par-ee"—Julia knew that this was the weird French way of saying *Paris*—"do you know what zey do to keep zee balance? Do you know what zey do with zese stu-peed baby toes?"

Daisy shook her head, her eyes as big as volley-balls.

Pound!

"ZEY CHOP ZEM OFF!" Madame Robes-pierre hollered.

Pound!

"*ZAT* IS WHAT ZEY DO TO ZEE BABY TOES!"

Pound pound!

"Any girl who falls oh-verrrr tonight," Madame screeched, "we will chop off zer toes!"

And just like that, she marched off the stage, her heels clackity-clickity-clackity-clicking.

Julia crossed out *MEAN* in her notebook and drew a picture of the Wicked Witch of the West.

On the other side of the curtain, the orchestra began to play. The ballerinas scrambled to their places.

Julia was worried.

What if Daisy really did fall over?

What if Madame Robespierre really did chop off her baby toes?

Was that why Sophie had asked Julia to come? Was that the big scoop she'd been talking about?

Just before the curtain rose, Julia noticed something across the stage. On the side opposite her, crouching under a folding table just like she was, there was a small, blond person.

Not just any small, blond person.

Sophie Simon.

Sophie was reading a book.

The curtain went up, and the audience cheered. The lights were bright and the music was loud.

Julia could see Daisy's parents in the very first row.

The ballerinas began to twirl, their giant, ugly hats spinning above them.

They twirled once.

They twirled twice.

Three times they twirled.

And four.

And five.

Daisy, so far, had not fallen over.

Julia wanted to write *LOTS OF TWIRLING* in her notebook, but she was too busy staring at Daisy.

On the one hand, Julia *really really* did *NOT* want Daisy to fall over. If Daisy fell over, she was going to be two toes short of a full set. And that would be a very bad thing.

On the other hand, Julia *really really DID* want Daisy to fall over. If Daisy fell over, there would definitely be something newsworthy to write about. And that would be a very good thing.

This, Julia thought, was what Miss Harbinger would call "a reporter's dilemma."

As she finished the tenth twirl, Daisy Pete began to look queasy.

On the fifteenth twirl, her face was as green as a toad's.

On the seventeenth twirl, the tip of the tower on top of her hat began to wobble.

On the eighteenth twirl, it wibbled.

And on the nineteenth twirl, in front of Madame Robespierre and her parents and everyone, Daisy Pete fell right smack on the ground.

The hat tumbled off her head and onto the stage.

The Eiffel Tower broke in half.

Julia gasped.

The audience gasped.

The *ballerinas* gasped.

The orchestra stopped playing, and the girls onstage stopped dancing.

Daisy Pete looked like she was going to cry.

Everyone was waiting—waiting, waiting, *waiting*—to see what would happen.

But just as Madame Robespierre leaped out of her seat—to chop off Daisy's baby toes, or possibly worse—Julia heard a holler from the other side of the stage.

"Remember what I told you!" the voice bellowed.

It was Sophie Simon, her fists balled up at her waist.

All of the ballerinas turned to look at her.

"Remember!" she shouted to them. "Fight for what's right! Just follow Daisy!"

And just like that, every single one of the ballerinas hiked up her tutu and sat down on the stage to join Daisy where she lay in a crumbled heap.

Madame Robespierre bounded up the stage steps two at a time.

She did not look pleased.

"WHAT IS GO-ING ON?" she hollered at her dancers.

Daisy sat up slowly. She looked at Madame Robespierre, and for the first time all night, Julia thought she didn't look afraid.

Julia placed her pencil over her notebook and got ready.

Something important was about to happen, she just knew it.

Daisy smiled at Madame Robespierre, a slow stretch of a smile that showed all her teeth.

"Madame Robespierre," Daisy said. "We're not going to dance anymore. Not until your"—Daisy glanced over at Sophie—"until your tyrannical domination over this dance company has ceased."

The audience began to murmur, and Julia did
her best to spell *TYRANNICAL DOMINATION*
in her notebook.

Madame Robespierre glared at Daisy.

"What is zese joke?" she hissed at her.

"It's not a joke," Daisy said, firmer this time.
"We're staging a sit-in."

The other girls nodded.

"By sitting on the stage."

"A SEET-IN!" Madame hollered. *Pound!* "Ballerinas do not seet!" *Pound!* "Zey dance!"

Madame shouted at the orchestra to start playing again. But even as the music swelled around them, the ballerinas refused to dance.

They just sat.

Julia could see the people in the audience shaking their heads and whispering to each other.

"DANCE!" Madame screeched. She tried to lift Daisy to her feet, but Daisy's body hung like a limp noodle, and she refused to stand up.

Madame tried to lift the other girls, but they made their bodies limp, too.

They didn't look much like ballerinas, Julia thought.

They looked more like boiled broccoli.

Not one of the dancers was going to dance.

Now this, Julia thought, was a news story.

Julia set down her notebook and picked up her camera. As Madame pounded her stick on the ground, trying to haul her dancers to their feet at the same time, Julia clicked photographs.

Click!

Pound!

Click!

Pound!

Click click click!

POUND!

"YOU ARE ZEE BALLERINAS!" Madame Robespierre bellowed. Her hair was flying from her bun in frightening wisps. "YOU WILL *DANCE*!"

Julia took another photo.

One by one, parents rose from their seats and climbed to the stage to scoop their pink-tutued daughters into their arms and walk out of the theater.

And as they exited the stage, Julia noticed that each girl handed Sophie Simon what appeared to be a five-dollar bill.

By the time Mr. and Mrs. Pete got to the stage, Daisy was the last ballerina left.

"Madame Robespierre," Mr. Pete said. "I think I speak for everyone in this town when I say that my daughter will *not* be attending your school of dance ever again. I'll be talking to the school board immediately and asking for your resignation. Your days in this business are over."

He turned to Daisy then, and held out a hand for her.

Daisy slowly rose to her feet.

She bent carefully at the waist.

She took a long, deep bow.

The audience went wild with applause.

Julia couldn't help but smile as Madame Robespierre ran off the stage.

She knew for a fact that her story was going to make the paper this time. She even had the perfect headline.

ROBESPIERRE GETS THE AX.

Now, she thought, if only she could figure out a way for her best friend, Owen, to get that rabbit he'd been wanting for his birthday . . .

The Lemur at the
Pool Party

Sophie's parents often drove Sophie bananas.

But they had never driven Sophie more bananas than on that Sunday afternoon, as they dropped her off at Owen Luu's birthday party.

"Oh, dill pickle!" Sophie's mother gushed as they walked into the backyard. Kids were already swimming and splashing in the pool. The girls were wearing bathing suits, and the boys were wearing swim trunks. Everyone was giggling and happy and looked thrilled to be at a birthday pool party.

Everyone, that is, except Owen and Sophie.

Owen was wearing green dolphin trunks with a dress shirt and tie.

Sophie had cargo pants on over her swimsuit, and her pockets were stuffed with objects she'd sneaked from home.

Very, very strange objects.

Objects she thought might come in handy.

"Oh, isn't this exciting, jelly bean?" Sophie's mother went on. "You're going to have so much fun!"

Sophie rolled her eyes to the right. She had *not* come to the party to have fun.

"Yes, biscuit!" Sophie's father exclaimed. "I think this will be the perfect place for you to make some friends!"

Sophie rolled her eyes to the left. She had *not* come to the party to make friends.

Sophie Simon had come to the birthday party to make sure Owen got his rabbit.

Then he would give her twenty dollars, and Sophie could finally buy the graphing calculator of her dreams.

The Pembo Q-60.

The latest model.

She turned to her parents.

"Mom?" she said. "Dad? Can you guys leave now?"

"Oh, Maxwell," Sophie's mother said to her

husband. "Did you hear that? Our little pudding pop wants nothing to do with us." She wiped away a tear. "Isn't that *wonderful*?"

Sophie's father nodded. "She's pushing away her caretakers," he said. "Just like Doctor Wanda was talking about last Wednesday."

"Our little banana cream pie is finally becoming well-adjusted."

"Mom?" Sophie said. "Dad? Seriously, will you leave?"

"Of course, my darling little lettuce wedge," her father said. "Here." He handed Sophie a sparkly blue gift bag. "Don't forget Owen's present. I hope he likes what you picked out."

"Mmm-hmm," Sophie said.

She wasn't listening.

She was looking around for Daisy.

"Goodbye, my apple crumble!" her mother said, kissing her on the left cheek.

"Have fun, wonton!" her father said, kissing her on the right cheek.

Sophie waited for her parents to leave, and then she wiped off both her cheeks. An "apple crumble" plus a "wonton" was enough to make her seriously ill.

Sophie spotted Daisy by the present table. She

was leaning over a wooden crate, making chirping noises.

Either Daisy had lost her mind, Sophie thought, or inside that crate was a ring-tailed lemur.

She went over to see which it was.

"Hi, Sophie!" Daisy called to her. "Do you want to meet Lenny the Lemur?"

Sophie bent down and peeked through the slats of the crate.

Staring back at her was a ring-tailed lemur. It looked just like the one Sophie had seen in the flyer outside the pet store.

The lemur had very short ears.

The lemur had a long, bushy tail.

"Yap!"

The lemur had a very noisy yap.

"Perfect," Sophie said.

Lenny the Lemur was the exact opposite of a rabbit.

"Where did you get him?" she asked Daisy.

Daisy poked a finger through the crate to rub Lenny's fur. "My cousin Matilda runs a rescue center for exotic animals. She's letting me borrow him for the day."

Sophie nodded. "And Mrs. Luu thinks this is the pet your parents picked for Owen?"

"Yep," Daisy said.

"Yap!" Lenny yapped.

"And your parents don't suspect anything?"

"Nope," Daisy said. "I told them Owen's mom called and said she changed her mind."

"Yap!" Lenny yapped.

"I think," Sophie said, "that everything will work out perfectly."

When all of the guests had arrived, Mrs. Luu told them they were going to open presents first.

Owen began to unwrap his gifts. Everyone crowded around him to see what presents he got.

Everyone, that is, except Sophie.

Sophie didn't care what presents Owen got. Unless he unwrapped a graphing calculator, she wasn't interested.

Owen did not unwrap a graphing calculator.

He unwrapped board games and card games and video games and loads of other stuff that Sophie found extremely boring.

From Julia, he got a box of rabbit food.

From Daisy, he got a rabbit cage.

From Sophie, he got an empty blue bag.

Owen turned the bag upside down.

"Where's my present?" he asked.

"Oh," Sophie said. "I guess I forgot to put it in there. But you can keep the bag if you want."

"Um, thanks," Owen said.

"You're welcome," Sophie told him.

Mrs. Luu clapped her hands together. "And now, Owen," she said, "it's time to give you *my* present."

She pulled the crate out from under the table.

She pried off the lid.

Inside was Lenny the Lemur.

At last, Sophie thought. *Now* things were getting interesting.

Lenny leaped out of the crate and scrambled onto Owen's shoulder, cuddling in the nook by his neck.

Owen looked like he'd rather spend an hour on the tilt-a-whirl after drinking a barrel of pickle juice than be snuggled around the neck by a ringtailed lemur.

"Isn't he *fantastic*, Owen?" Mrs. Luu cried. "It's exactly what you wanted!"

"I-I . . . It's . . . I . . ." Lenny was licking his claws and staring at Owen. Owen gulped. "It-it . . . I . . ."

Sophie poked him in the side.

"It's perfect," Owen said. He gulped again. "It's exactly the exact same pet I wanted. Exactly."

"I knew you would love it!" Mrs. Luu exclaimed. "Now! Time for cake!"

While Mrs. Luu lit the candles, Sophie thought about the most recent book she'd checked out from the library.

Fascinating Facts About Ring-Tailed Lemurs

She thought about one chapter in particular.

"The Diet of the Ring-Tailed Lemur"

There were lots of interesting bits of information in that chapter, but there was one fact that Sophie had found *especially* fascinating:

One of a lemur's favorite snacks is grasshoppers.

Mrs. Luu finished lighting the candles.

Sophie scooched to the very back of the crowd of kids, far away from Mrs. Luu.

"Everybody sing!" Mrs. Luu called out.

"Happy birthday to you!" they all sang.

Sophie reached inside her right pocket.

"Happy birthday to you!"

She pulled out a handful of grasshoppers she'd found in her yard.

"Happy birthday, dear Owen!"

She tossed the grasshoppers up in the air, and they landed—*plunk plunk plunk plunk*—right on top of the cake.

"Happy bir—"

"YAP!"

Lenny the Lemur leaped from Owen's shoulder and pounced onto the cake, trying to grab the grasshoppers.

He snuffed out the candles.

"Yap!"

The cake toppled over.

"Yap!"

Fur and frosting went flying.

"Yap!"

"Owen, your birthday cake!" Mrs. Luu screamed. She yanked Lenny out of the frosting and dropped him on the grass. "I spent seventeen hours perfecting the icing! And now it's *ruined*!"

Sophie smiled.

"Th-that's okay, Mom," Owen said slowly. "I

don't mind. That lemur is the exact pet I exactly
wanted. Exactly."

Mrs. Luu sniffed. "Well," she said, examining
the frosted, ice creamy lemur at her feet. "Okay
then. I'm glad you're so happy. I guess it's time
for the high-dive contest."

While Mrs. Luu led the children to the diving
board, Sophie scooped up Lenny the Lemur and
set him on her shoulder.

Lenny licked his cakey claws, and Sophie winked at him.

Sophie thought about another chapter in the book about lemurs.

"The Social Habits of the Ring-Tailed Lemur"

There were tons of exciting pieces of information in that chapter, but there was one fact that Sophie had found *especially* remarkable:

When lemurs get cold, they like to warm their bellies in the sun. They can stay perfectly still for hours.

Mrs. Luu snapped her fingers. "Everybody in line for the diving board!" she cried.

Everyone lined up behind the diving board ladder.

Sophie stood at the back of the line, Lenny perched on her shoulder.

She reached inside her left pocket.

She pulled out the battery-powered fan she'd brought from home.

She turned the fan on high and shot the frosty air at the ice-cream-covered lemur.

"*YAP!*"

Lenny leaped from her shoulder and raced up the ladder.

He plopped himself down—*PLOP!*—in the sunny spot at the very center of the diving board.

"Oh no!" Mrs. Luu shouted, staring up at the lemur high above the pool. He had his belly to the sun, his little lemur arms out to the sides. "How can we have a high-dive contest when there's a *lemur* on the diving board?"

Owen shrugged.

He did not seem very upset about not being able to dive.

Mrs. Luu stomped to the front of the line and climbed the ladder.

She walked to the edge, one wobbly footstep at a time.

She tried to pry Lenny off the diving board.

She poked and prodded.

"*Yap!*"

The diving board flopped, and Mrs. Luu bounced. Down below, the kids held their breath. But Mrs. Luu kept her balance and did not fall into the pool.

She tugged and tickled.

"Yap!"

The diving board flipped, and Mrs. Luu bobbed. Down below, the kids held their breath. But Mrs. Luu kept her balance and did not fall into the pool.

She jerked and jostled.

"YAP!"

The diving board flip-flip-flop-flop-flipped, and Mrs. Luu bumped and bopped and bucked. Down below, the kids held their breath. But Mrs. Luu kept her balance.

She did not fall into the pool.

And that lemur would not move a muscle.

"I had this diving board installed especially for your birthday extravaganza!" Mrs. Luu wailed across the water. "And now the high-dive contest is *ruined*!"

Sophie smiled.

"I–I don't mind, Mom," Owen said. "Really. I still exactly love that exact lemur exactly up there."

"Well," she said once she had climbed down the ladder. "As long as you're happy, Owen." She looked up at Lenny and shook her head. "I guess it's time for the old-fashioned taffy pull."

While Mrs. Luu set out the pot of taffy mixture on the table, Sophie thought about Chapter 3 in the book about lemurs.

"Predators of the Ring-Tailed Lemur"

There were loads of incredible nuggets of information in that chapter, but there was one fact that Sophie had found *especially* amazing.

One of a lemur's fiercest enemies is the Madagascar ground boa. If confronted with a boa constrictor, a lemur will attack.

Mrs. Luu pointed to the pot of syrupy taffy mixture. "Who wants to add the food coloring?" she asked.

Sophie looked at the bottles of food coloring.

She picked up a bottle labeled "Jungle Green."

"I'll do it," she said.

She unscrewed the lid.

"Just a tiny titch," Mrs. Luu told her.

Sophie nodded.

She poured in a tiny titch.

Then she poured in the tiniest titch more.

"That's enough," Mrs. Luu told her.

"Okay," Sophie said.

She grinned at Owen.

And then she poured in the whole bottle.

"Whoops," she said. "It must have slipped."

Mrs. Luu took the bottle from Sophie and frowned at her.

"Now," Mrs. Luu told the children after she had stirred in the dye, "in order to turn this mixture into candy, we have to pull it. I'll show you. You just grab a great glob like this"—Mrs. Luu reached in the pot—"and then you take it in both your hands"—she took hold of a heaping blob of dark green goop—"and you stretch it."

Mrs. Luu began to pull.

Slowly . . .

Slowly . . .

Longer . . .

And longer . . .

Until the taffy between her hands looked exactly like one long, thin, green—

"Yap!"

—snake.

"Yap yap!"

A Madagascar ground boa, to be exact.

"Yap yap yap!"

From up on his high-dive perch, Lenny had spotted the taffy.

"What on earth," Mrs. Luu said, the taffy stretched out between her hands, "is that lemur yapping abou—"

"YAP!"

That's when she was kicked in the taffy by a high-diving lemur.

"YAP!"

Lenny scuffled with the taffy, and Mrs. Luu knocked over the taffy pot.

CRASH!

"YAP!"

Mrs. Luu hollered.

Lenny tussled with the taffy, and Mrs. Luu toppled onto the table.

BASH!

"YAP!"

Mrs. Luu screamed.

Lenny wrestled with the taffy, and Mrs. Luu, her feet just inches from the edge of the pool . . .

Lost her balance . . .

And tumbled into the water.

SPLASH!

"YAP!"

Mrs. Luu wailed.

"That's it!" Mrs. Luu screeched from the water. She climbed out of the pool.

Her dress was soaked.

Her shoe was broken.

Her hair was stuck to her eyebrows.

The taffy was toast.

"I tried out twenty-two different recipes to make that taffy!" Mrs. Luu bellowed. "And that lemur *ruined* it! He ruined *everything*!"

Sophie smiled.

"But I *love* the lemur," Owen said. He scooped Lenny out of the pool and handed him to Daisy, sticky and dripping and taffyed all over. "He's exactly the pet I wanted. Exactly."

"Well, I'm sorry, Owen," Mrs. Luu said. She wrung out her sleeves. "But I never should have agreed to get you such an exotic pet. I knew it was a mistake from the beginning."

She squeezed the water out of her hair.

"A lemur clearly isn't a good pet for you," she said. "You need something totally different. Like a rabbit. Yes. A nice, quiet rabbit with long ears and a fluffy little tail."

Owen nodded slowly. "Yeah, Mom," he said. "That doesn't sound too ba—"

"No arguments!" Mrs. Luu scolded. "You're

getting a rabbit and there's nothing you can do to change my mind!"

Owen slipped Sophie a twenty-dollar bill.

"I guess that's fine then," he told his mother.

Sophie smiled and tucked the bill in her pocket with the rest of her money.

One hundred dollars.

Sophie finally had one hundred dollars.

She had done it. She had thought of every detail and solved every problem. And now she had exactly enough money to get the Pembo Q-60.

Mrs. Luu took off her shoes and dumped out the pool water. "I'm going to call Petes' Pets right now and ask for my money back," she said.

Sophie stopped smiling.

It turned out there was *one* detail she hadn't thought of.

"What?" she asked Mrs. Luu.

"I'm going to call the pet store," Mrs. Luu said. "I paid one hundred dollars for that lemur, and I want my money back."

And she turned and walked, drippy-sticky, toward the house.

"Sophie!" Daisy hissed. "She can't call my parents! I'll get in trouble! What if they make me go back to ballet class?"

Julia's eyes were big as cantaloupes. "If Daisy goes back to ballet class," she cried, "then I won't have a news story!"

Owen sat down plop in the grass. "If my mom finds out about the lemur," he said, "she'll *never* get me a rabbit!"

Sophie stuck her hand inside her pocket.

One hundred dollars.

She looked at Daisy.

She looked at Julia.

She looked at Owen.

Sophie sighed.

"Mrs. Luu!" she called out.

Mrs. Luu turned.

"You don't need to call the pet store!" Sophie hollered.

Mrs. Luu walked back to the pool.

"Daisy has your refund," Sophie said. She took the money out of her pocket and slipped it secretly into Daisy's hand. "One hundred dollars. Her parents made her bring it in case there was a problem."

Daisy looked at the money, and then she looked at Sophie.

Sophie nodded.

Daisy handed the money to Mrs. Luu.

"Thank you," Mrs. Luu said. She walked back inside the house, leaving soggy footsteps all the way.

And then something happened to Sophie that had never happened before.

Daisy hugged her.

And Julia hugged her.

And *Owen* hugged her.

"Sophie!" Julia cried. The four of them were squeezed up tight together like a human snowball. "I think you may just be the best friend I've ever, ever had."

And Owen and Daisy agreed.

Sophie thought about that.

Somehow, Sophie had not ended up with a calculator.

Somehow, she had ended up with friends.

What on earth was she supposed to do with *those*?

If Sophie Simon had been paying attention during the rest of the party, instead of sulking behind the broken cake table with the soggy, taffy-covered lemur, she would have noticed several things.

She would have noticed Daisy whispering to Owen.

She would have noticed Owen whispering to Julia.

And she would have noticed that when Julia's father, Professor McGreevy, showed up early to talk to his daughter about long division, Julia whispered to him.

But Sophie didn't notice any of those things.

By the time Sophie's parents came to pick her up, she was miserable.

Sad.

Sullen.

Sunk.

"Hello, sweet potato!" her father greeted her. "Did you make any friends?"

"Yes," Sophie said with a sigh. "I'm afraid I did. I don't really want to talk about it."

"Oh, Maxwell," Sophie's mother said to her husband. "Did you hear that? Our little garbanzo bean is being rude and ill-mannered." She clutched her chest. "Isn't that *fabulous*?"

Sophie's father nodded. "She's refusing to talk about her personal life," he said. "Just like that well-adjusted child on Doctor Wanda's show last Thursday."

Sophie was in the middle of rolling her eyes to the right and then back again, when she heard a voice behind her.

"Excuse me."

Sophie turned around.

It was Julia's father, Professor McGreevy.

"My daughter Julia tells me there's a girl over here who's very good at math," he said. He looked at Sophie. "Would that be you?"

Sophie looked over at the pool. Owen, Daisy, and Julia were laughing and splashing each other with pool water.

"Yes," Sophie said. "I'm good at math."

"But only in a well-adjusted way," her father piped in.

"The well-adjusted amount of good," her mother added.

"Why do you want to know?" Sophie asked.

"Well," Professor McGreevy said. "Since it seems Julia won't be on the Math Olympics team this year, we're short one mathlete. And I thought you might like to join."

He turned to Sophie's parents. "It would be a great opportunity for your daughter to make friends," he told them.

"Tater Tot, did you hear that?" her mother cried. "More friends!"

Her father nodded. "Oh, lemon wedge, you could have a whole gaggle of them!"

"It's very fun," Professor McGreevy said. "Mathletically, I mean. There's a large competition, very competitive, and . . ."

Sophie stopped listening.

She did not want to join Math Olympics.

She did not want a whole gaggle of friends.

What Sophie *wanted* was a—

". . . calculator."

Sophie's head shot up.

"What did you say?" she asked Professor Mc-Greevy.

"I said," he repeated, "that each mathlete on the winning team gets a graphing calculator." Sophie's ears perked up. "The Pembo Q-60." Sophie stood a little straighter. "It's the latest model," he concluded.

Sophie looked over to the far end of the pool again.

Julia, Owen, and Daisy waved at her.

They were all grinning.

"So," Professor McGreevy said, "will you join us?"

Sophie waved back at Julia, Owen, and Daisy.

She was grinning, too.

"Sophie?" Professor McGreevy asked.

Maybe, Sophie thought, just maybe, she might actually like having friends.

"Yes," she said. "I think I might like that quite a bit."

Sophie Simon's Encyclopedia of Things She Can't Believe You Don't Know Already

antigravity boots: Boots with large springs on the bottom which allow the wearer to jump very high and far, as though he were on the moon (or on his way to the hospital).

calculus: A very difficult type of math, used to calculate volumes and formulaic changes. Most third-graders hate it more than chocolate-covered beetles.

civil disobedience: A form of protest in which people purposefully refuse to obey certain laws or rules that they feel are unfair without behaving in a violent manner. Many famous leaders, including Mahatma Gandhi and Martin Luther King, Jr., used this technique in their struggles for equal rights, and they often called in news reporters to cover the protests.

earthworm: A worm that lives in the earth. Earthworms have five "hearts," which are very different from the hearts inside humans but just as difficult to operate on.

Eiffel Tower: An iron tower in Paris, France, designed by the engineer Gustave Eiffel for the 1889 World's Fair. Over 1,000 feet tall, it stands higher than the Chrysler Building in New York City and weighs over 10,000 tons. Not a very good subject for a hat.

flan: A dessert, popular in Spain and Mexico, that is made from sugar, eggs, and milk. Sort of like pudding but wigglier.

frogs' legs: A favorite French food, often fried and served with a healthy heaping of garlic. Yum yum!

Mahatma Gandhi (1869–1948): A political and spiritual leader in India during that country's independence movement, famous for his belief in nonviolence. After the British government placed a tax on common salt—making it very difficult for many Indian citizens to pay for the necessary item—Gandhi led one of his most successful protests, the Salt March to Dandi in 1930, walking over 200 miles to the ocean in order to collect his own salt illegally.

graphing calculator: A type of calculator used to chart graphs and study calculus. Most third-graders would rather have a pony.

Greensboro sit-ins: A series of peaceful protests that helped spark the African-American civil rights movement in the United States. In February 1960, several African-American college students sat down at a "whites-only" lunch counter in a Woolworth's store in Greensboro, North Carolina, even though they knew they would not be served. After many similar protests, Woolworth's and other stores around the country changed their rules, serving anyone regardless of race.

Math Olympics: Just like the regular Olympics, but with math instead of sports. Also, with smaller medals.

Sir Isaac Newton (1642–1727): A physicist and mathematician famous for numerous achievements, including sitting around and watching apples fall, and inventing calculus. Sophie thinks he's amazing. Julia, not so much.

reverse psychology: A method of getting people to do what you want them to by convincing them that you want the exact opposite. Very useful for extending allowances and bedtimes.

ring-tailed lemur: A primate most easily recognized by its long, black-and-white-ringed tail. Ring-tailed lemurs are native to the island of Madagascar, eat mainly plants and bugs, and occasionally get into fights, although usually with other male lemurs and not with taffy. They often sit in the sun for long periods of time, with their arms out to their sides and their bellies stretched up toward the sky, in what is known as their "sun-worshiping" position. Loud and ferocious, they make terrible pets (sorry, Lenny).

Robespierre: A surname most typically associated with Maximilien Robespierre (1758–1794), an official who ordered the execution of so many people during the French Revolution that his period of leadership is known as the Reign of Terror. Like many of his victims, he was eventually beheaded. No one knows for sure if Madame Robespierre is one of Maximilien's descendants, but chances are good that she is.

Saltwater taffy: A very sticky type of candy that needs to be pulled before it can be eaten. It is never made with either salt water or boa constrictors. See following page for a recipe.

sit-in: A nonviolent form of protest in which people sit in one place and refuse to leave until their demands are met. Very useful in changing government policy, or in ending a horrible dance recital.

topographic map: A type of map that shows how tall or short things are, from mountains to riverbeds. Not typically made out of mashed potatoes.

How to Make Madagascar Ground Boa Taffy

Saltwater taffy is almost as much fun to make as it is to eat. Since the mixture gets extremely hot, you should only try this recipe with the help of an adult.

What you'll need:

2 cups sugar
2 tablespoons cornstarch
1 cup light corn syrup
¾ cup water
2 tablespoons butter, cut into small pieces
1 teaspoon salt

1 teaspoon flavoring (such as vanilla, lemon, maple, or mint)
green food coloring
extra butter for greasing

cookie sheet with raised edges, or shallow baking dish
very large saucepan (3- to 4-quart)
wooden spoon
candy thermometer
small bowl filled with cold water
waxed paper
cooking scissors, or a butter knife, greased with butter

What to do:

1. Grease the cookie sheet or baking dish with butter and set it aside.
2. In the saucepan, mix together the sugar and cornstarch. Add the corn syrup, water, 2 tablespoons of butter, and salt.
3. Place the saucepan over medium heat, and stir constantly until the sugar dissolves and the mixture begins to boil, about 10 to 15 minutes.
4. Let the mixture continue to boil, without

stirring, and insert candy thermometer, until it reads 270°F. This will take about 15 minutes.

5. Test the mixture by spooning a small amount of it into the bowl of cold water. The mixture should solidify into thin strands that are flexible, not brittle. Remove the strands from the water. If you can form them into a ball in your hand, the mixture is not hot enough and needs to boil a while longer. If the strands bend slightly before breaking, you have reached the perfect temperature.

6. Remove the saucepan from the heat. Add the flavoring and food coloring (about 5 to 20 drops, depending on how dark you want the taffy to be), and stir gently.

7. Pour the mixture onto the cookie sheet or into the baking dish, and let it sit until it hardens slightly and is cool enough to handle, about 15 to 20 minutes.

8. Grease your hands with butter. Take about a third of the taffy mixture from the cookie sheet and pull it between your hands, stretching it out and then folding it back on itself, and stretching again. Continue to pull the taffy until it becomes lighter and has a satiny gloss, about 7 to 10 minutes. Look out for flying lemurs!

9. Roll the pulled taffy into a long, thin snake, about ½ inch in diameter, and cut it with the greased scissors or knife into 1-inch-long pieces. Repeat steps 8 and 9 until you have pulled and cut all of the taffy.

10. Let the taffy pieces sit for about 30 minutes, then wrap in small squares of waxed paper, twisting the ends.

Makes about 50 pieces

LISA GRAFF, shown here in her third-grade school photo, lives in New York City. She is the author of three middle-grade novels, including *The Thing About Georgie* and *Umbrella Summer*, both nominated for the Texas Bluebonnet Award. A former associate children's book editor, she now devotes herself to writing full-time.

JASON BEENE, also shown in third grade, has worked extensively in the game industry since graduating from the Rhode Island School of Design. This is his first book. He lives in Providence, Rhode Island.

fOREWORD

by Sylvia Boorstein,
author of *It's Easier Than You Think:
The Buddhist Way to Happiness*

In 1990, James Baraz and I traveled to India with some of our friends to visit the venerable Advaita teacher, Sri H. W. L. Poonja, in Lucknow. Every day for three weeks we traveled (on three-wheel taxis, then pedal-rickshaw, then on foot) to arrive in time for morning *darshan* (teachings) with Poonjaji. We sat squeezed in close to each other on the floor of Poonjaji's small living room, along with perhaps twenty other students from all over the world. Poonjaji sat on a raised platform in the front of the room and talked and taught and laughed for hours, including each of us, one by one, in dialogue. We loved it. And at the end, Poonjaji agreed to see James and me in a private interview.

"What do you teach?" he asked.

James answered, "We teach Mindfulness and Metta, and we specifically emphasize *dana* (generosity)."

"There is no such *thing* as generosity," Poonjaji said. (James and I exchanged glances that said, "Uh-oh! Have we just started to present ourselves and done it wrong?")

"No such thing at all," Poonjaji continued. "There is only the arising of need, and the natural impulse of the heart to address it. If you are hungry and your hand puts food in your mouth, you don't think of the hand as generous, do you? If someone in front of you is hungry, and you put food in their mouth, it's the same, isn't it?"

James and I talked afterward. "Maybe he's right," I said. "Let's think this through. When I put away my winter clothing, I think, 'This I didn't wear at all: Salvation Army. This I wore a little bit. Hmmm. I *could* save it, I *could* give it to the Salvation Army. I'll give it away!' Isn't that generosity?"

"Maybe it's mindful-awareness-of-the-presence-of-lust or mindful-awareness-of-the-absence-of-lust," James said. "No *one* who is generous."

"Hmmm," I thought. I've continued to think about it for ten years.

I think there is no *one* who is generous, but there *is* generosity. Generosity is a habit of mind, a tendency, a capacity. It is the antidote for lust. It enables the mind to relax when it gets tied in knots of clinging. It conditions thoughts like, "Maybe I *don't* need this," and "Probably I'll feel happier sharing." It does create happiness. When we feel we have enough, when we feel satisfied, when we feel, "My cup is brimming," we are unafraid. We are at ease. We are happy!

The Buddha named Generosity as the first of the Ten *Paramitas* (Perfected Qualities) of an enlightened mind. He suggested that people begin their conscious cultivation of the Paramitas with the practice of Generosity because it is the simplest. Everyone, he said, has something they could give away, and the act of giving brings gladness and joy to the mind. I was encouraged when I heard about *cultivating* Paramitas. It meant to me that I didn't need to wait until *after* enlightenment—if, and whenever, that might happen—to manifest these lovely qualities. And, I was thrilled to hear accounts of many, many people, in the time of the Buddha, who became completely enlightened just by hearing him speak. The written accounts usually end with the phrase, "and their minds, through not clinging, were liberated from taints." They had generous minds. They let go of their old views. They gave themselves the gift of freedom.

I also understand the nine other Paramitas, those that follow Generosity in the traditional list, as elaborated forms of Generosity. They are *all* gifts. Morality gives the people we meet the gift of safety and gives us what the Buddha called "the bliss of blamelessness."

Renunciation gives us the gift of a calmed-down lust system, which moves us to cherish and appreciate what we already have. When we practice Restraint, we give ourselves the gift of self-confidence, the assurance that our impulse system will not take off on its own. When we are Patient, we give ourselves the gift of reflection and wise choice. When we are Honest we give ourselves and the people with whom we are honest the gift of intimacy. When I give myself the gift of Energy—by taking quiet time in my days, retreat time in my life, bicycle time for my body—I reconnect with what I *know* to be true. The energy of that reconnection sustains my relationships with the people I meet.

If I am able to love and forgive myself—not always easy—I will be able to be a gift of kindness to anyone I meet. When I practice Equanimity—making my mind still enough and wide enough and balanced enough—to hold the whole universe of stories with the Wisdom that sees them as conditioned links in a lawful cosmos of connections—I am able to cry hard and laugh loud and feel whole.

Poonjaji was right about no *one* being generous. When I feel whole, when I don't feel needy, I forget myself. I share more. I become kinder. In the end, Generosity becomes the great Act of Kindness that sustains the world.

My grandfather lived with my family for some years, when he was in his middle nineties. The story he liked most to tell, when people asked him how he liked living with us, was one in which Smokey, our very friendly old Labrador Retriever, had once again gotten through the gate and made his way to the grade school three blocks away. The children there loved him, and the teachers used him as a therapy for children who had dog fears, but the Humane Society came by every morning and picked up all dogs off leashes, and Smokey had been "arrested" many times.

"The school called me," my grandfather would say, "and told me, 'Smokey is here. Come quickly before the Pound comes.' So I rushed to school as fast as I could with the leash, and the bell for the end of school rang just as Smokey and I were leaving. So, Emily walked with us."

Emily, my youngest child, was eight at the time. My grandfather was ninety-four.

He continued, "We had just started walking when suddenly it started to rain. Emily took off her rain-coat"—at that point in the story my grandfather always started to cry—"and said, 'Here, Grandpa. You wear this.'"

That was the story he told most.

xv

Opening Our Hearts and Hands

It's not the earthquake
That controls the advent of a different life
But storms of generosity....

—BORIS PASTERNAK

I was sitting in a café one day, waiting for a friend, when I noticed a middle-aged woman walking toward a nearby table, juggling three cups of coffee and the paraphernalia that goes along with them. She handed two of the cups over to two gentlemen who were sitting there. "Thank you," one of them said. "My pleasure," she replied and flashed such a radiant smile that I knew down to my bones that her simple act had brought her pleasure, and even happiness.

If you are like me, you want to be happy. Like me, you've probably spent a lot of time trying to be happy. Are you? A large study in England and the United States recently found that the number of Americans who consider themselves happy has been steadily declining over the past thirty years. I think it's because we're looking for happiness in all the wrong places.

The United States is currently undergoing the biggest sustained economic expansion in history, and the Internet and the stock market are creating multimillionaires left and right. It's all about making money these days. Even my peers, ex-lefties and hippies, talk about nothing but IPOs. Several young friends are regularly ridiculed by their peers for following their career passions instead of jumping into the dot-com craze. The clincher about where our contemporary values are came while I was watching the television show *Greed: The Series*. It's a game show in which contestants "climb the tower of greed," and give in to their "need for greed" when "The Terminator" allows one of them to get an automatic $10,000 if they challenge a teammate. I couldn't get over the fact that greed—a vice, a poison, something that spiritual traditions historically caution against—was now elevated so openly into something good, something to be joyously indulged in.

What is wrong with this picture?

I don't profess to have all the answers. All I know is that in my twenties and thirties, I was your average unhappy and fearful person. Then, about twelve years ago, through a series of circumstances, I began to refocus my life on what truly mattered and stopped being miserable. And that has made all the difference.

It started when I, along with several others, published the book *Random Acts of Kindness*.™ It seemed like a good idea at the time—let's all do nice little things for strangers—but once I began to see and hear about its effects, I sensed I had stumbled upon something very important. Suddenly I was inundated with letters from people telling me about the joy they had experienced as either doers or receivers of these acts. I will never forget the letter from a high school student who said he was going to kill himself until he read our book and decided that life was worth living. I became fascinated with the power of kindness, and went on to help write a series of books on the topic. I tried to enact what I was writing about and became more kind both to strangers and to those I am close to. Like the boy who didn't kill himself, I got happier.

I began to wonder about the other qualities that could produce the same positive effect as kindness, and turned my attention to gratitude. The more I cultivated a sense of appreciation for all that I had instead of focusing on what I lacked, the happier and less fearful I was. I wrote about my experiences, this time in *Attitudes of Gratitude*, and once again, I received many letters about the power gratitude has in bringing peace of mind and a sense of contentment.

My study of gratitude led me to generosity, the spontaneous giving of ourselves and our resources to someone else. In a sense, I have now come full circle.

Generosity is the mother of kindness. Our desire to give help, comfort, support, or appreciation is often the reason we do kind things.

In reading, talking, and thinking about generosity, I realized just how important it is. Boris Pasternak alludes to the power of generosity in the quote at the beginning of this chapter. We tend to think about generosity as volunteering or giving money or time, but generosity is actually much broader. It comes in all kinds of forms—material, intellectual, emotional, and spiritual. We can be generous when we give our knowledge, our awareness, our empathy, or our silence. Generosity is also about letting go of grudges, hurts, and concepts of ourselves and the world that stand in the way of our connection to others.

True generosity is open-heartedness, the experience and expression of our boundless, unconditionally loving nature. It is such an important concept that Buddhists consider its opposite to be delusion. When we are out of touch with our giving hearts, the natural flow of generosity within us, we think we need to hold on to money, possessions, and fixed ideas. We are sure we need these things to be happy, when our very grasping and clinging is what makes us miserable. We hold on so tightly that our hands are unavailable to reach out for the happiness we could gain by letting go. Our delusion of material happiness prevents us from being truly happy.

However, when we are living from true generosity, we feel expansive and abundant. We know that we can find true happiness in loving and being loved to the core of our being. Our hearts and hands are open, ready to offer what they can and able to receive what comes back to us in return.

As the woman in the café realized, giving makes us feel great. It's a fabulous feeling, even when we offer something as small as a cup of coffee. Giving lifts us out of our preoccupation with ourselves and reminds us that there is plenty of kindness to go around.

Like kindness and gratitude, giving—both of ourselves and our unique gifts—is actually very simple. So simple that it's often difficult to believe it can bring us such joy. We think giving should be hard, so we make it complicated. We guilt-trip ourselves into thinking we should give more or try harder, usually turning our guilt into shame, and then trying to avoid the whole issue entirely.

It doesn't have to be that way. The purpose of *A Giving Heart* is to provide encouragement. Encouragement in noticing that the river of generosity is already flowing in you, and encouragement in opening your heart as much as you feel comfortable and giving exactly as much as you want. It's about paying attention and noticing how you feel when you give, when it feels good and when it doesn't. Noticing the effects on your life and then choosing to do more of what makes you feel good.

I've come to understand that generosity is both a feeling—of fullness, of expansion, of joy—and a choice. The more we make the choice, the more we experience the feeling. This book charts a journey through attitudes and behaviors that I hope will allow you to open your heart more easily and frequently.

I am not setting myself up as an expert. If you met me, I don't think you'd be particularly struck by my generosity. Regard me as a fellow seeker on the path, a person who has often been quite fearful and stingy but who wants to change. Recently I read a novel about a girl with "a heart so clear you could see all the way through it." That's how openhearted I want to be. I've seen, and even tasted a bit for myself, the peace, joy, and sense of contentment that the giving heart can offer, and I want us all to share in more of that contentment.

I'm convinced that we are here on Earth to grow our souls, to open wider, to reach higher, and to stretch farther. Our goal is to soften where we would normally constrict, to loosen when we would habitually tighten, and to extend where we would usually hold back. Each and every one of us has so much to offer, and the world needs what we have to give.

The Gifts of Giving

Above all let us never forget that an act of goodness is an act of happiness.

—Count Maurice Maeterlinck

e begin by examining the bounty generosity can bring us whenever we open our hearts to another being. Understanding the rewards we will reap may motivate us to cultivate our own gifts and offer them wholeheartedly to the world. As we discover the grace that comes of giving, we begin to experience generosity as a natural upwelling of the heart that exists in each of us, and as a limitless treasure that can bring us immeasurable delight.

Giving Is a Great Mood Elevator

No joy can equal the joy of serving others.

—SAI BABA

It was one of those no-good rotten days in which nothing was going right for me. I had been up half the night with my daughter Ana, my computer kept crashing, and I got ten phone calls that distracted me from my writing. When I picked Ana up from preschool, I was in a less than stellar mood. I popped her into the car, and, still grumbling to myself, we headed for the grocery store.

At the store, the line seemed interminable. Finally I was the next one up, but it was still taking forever. Despite my annoyance, I tuned in to what was happening. The young woman in front of me kept asking the cashier to give her the total after each item. She had a tiny baby in her cart, and it was clear she didn't have enough money to pay for all the food she bought, so she went off to make a phone call, presumably to ask someone for money.

While she was gone, I asked the cashier to total up everything and tell her that she had enough money. I would make up the difference when she left. The cashier asked me if I knew her—I didn't—and then if I were wealthy. "Yes," I replied, thinking of my beautiful daughter, the roof over my head, and the privilege of doing work that I loved.

When I left the store, I realized I was singing along with the radio and feeling remarkably good. The best part of the situation was that the woman never realized what I had done. A bit puzzled, she had gladly wheeled her cart away. I smiled to myself. Reaching out to her had reset my mood, and I felt like I was in love with the whole world.

Helping others really is like a "feel good" pill. When I was doing the research for my last book, *365 Health and Happiness Boosters*, I realized that making someone else happy creates happiness the fastest. Lending a hand, making someone smile, or being of use to someone other than ourselves helps us stop focusing solely on our own difficulties and gives a larger perspective to our days. This is what Karl Marx meant when he said, "Experience praises the most happy the one who made the most people happy."

Giving Can Heal

*There is a wonderful, mystical law of nature that
the three things we crave most in life—happiness, freedom,
and peace of mind—are always attained
by giving them to someone else.*

—ANONYMOUS

During the break-up of a fourteen-year relationship, I was in terrible pain and leaned heavily on the love and advice of my friends, including author Daphne Rose Kingma, who flew up from Santa Barbara to sit with me for a few days. When she was about to leave, she gave me a tiny piece of paper, her prescription for my healing: (1) Go to therapy; (2) Meditate; (3) Reach out to others in pain.

I'm glad to say I did all three items. At the time, though, I didn't see why helping others would help me. I understood the benefits of therapy—working through the grief, coming to see my part in the break-up, and understanding the relationship dynamics I tend to encounter. I saw how meditation might work—tapping into the sense of peacefulness and wholeness beneath the pain of my situation. But giving to others? Wasn't this a time to focus on myself?

Once I began to volunteer at a "Meals on Wheels"

15

organization for people with AIDS, I learned that giving to others was also a way to help myself. Helping others forced me to notice something other than my own misery, which was a great gift. Rather than wallowing in all the ways I had been mistreated and abused, I could turn my attention to someone else. As months passed, however, I discovered something else. Walking the halls of the welfare hotel where most of my deliveries were, I stopped being so attached to my particular wound and began to see that suffering is part of life. All kinds of terrible things happen to people, often for no reason, and I was not specially singled out for victimization.

While it wasn't true for me in this situation, giving when you are feeling hurt often makes meaning out of your suffering. The person who's paralyzed by a gunshot wound and then becomes an advocate for gun control, the woman who finally escapes from her abusive husband and works to set up a shelter for battered women—these are individuals who reach up out of the particulars of their individual tragedies to ensure that others will not have to suffer the same fate.

You don't have to be suffering from some specific hurt to reap the benefits of giving. Any time we reach out to others—in our hurt or with our love—we feel better.

Giving Is Good for Our Health

It is one of the most beautiful compensations of life that no man
can sincerely try to help another without helping himself.

—RALPH WALDO EMERSON

I have a friend who has had a terrible case of lupus for nearly twenty years. She has been hospitalized many times and is constantly on medication that has horrible side effects, including cataracts. She had to quit her job as a graphic designer and now is completely supported by her husband. She can get really down about her life. Recently she decided to become a volunteer at a soup kitchen. She goes when she feels up to it, and she's started to discover that the more she goes, the better she feels—emotionally and physically. Her arthritis (a consequence of lupus) isn't as severe and she has more energy.

Helping others can not only make us feel good about ourselves; it can also increase our physical well-being. The mind and body aren't separate. Anything we do to elevate our spirits will also have a beneficial effect on our health. A recent study by Cornell University found that volunteering increases a person's energy, sense of mastery over life, and self-esteem. Other studies have demonstrated that such positive feelings can

17

actually strengthen and enhance the immune system. Positive emotions increase the body's number of T-cells, cells in the immune system that help the body resist disease and recover quickly from illness. Positive emotions also release endorphins into the bloodstream. Endorphins are the body's natural tranquilizers and painkillers; they stimulate dilation of the blood vessels, which leads to a relaxed heart.

While we don't quite understand all the reasons why giving creates good health, many studies have documented generosity's positive effects. Michigan researchers who studied 2,700 people for almost ten years found that men who regularly did volunteer work had death rates two-and-one half times lower than men who didn't. In a separate study, volunteers who worked directly with those who benefited from their services had a greater immune system boost than those whose volunteer work was restricted to pushing papers.

Harvard researchers also conducted a study that showed how giving is such a powerful immune booster that it can be experienced just by watching someone else in the act of giving! In this well-known experiment, students looking at a film of Mother Teresa as she tended the sick in Calcutta—even those who purported to dislike Mother Teresa—got an increase in immune function.

Psychologist Robert Ornstein and physician David Sobel are well known for their examinations of the health effects of altruism. In their book *Healthy Pleasures*, they describe what they call the "helper's high," a kind of euphoria volunteers get when helping others—a warm glow in the chest and a sense of vitality that comes from being simultaneously energized and calm. They compare it to a runner's high and claim it is caused by the body's release of endorphins. Because of all these health benefits, as Stella Reznick says in *The Pleasure Zone*, "the one who ends up getting the most from a good deed may, ultimately, be the good Samaritan."

Generosity Alleviates Fear

*It is expressly at those times when we feel needy
that we will benefit the most from giving.*

—Ruth Ross

I 've never had the privilege of meeting writer Anne Lamott, but I have loved her books, particularly *Operating Instructions.* Her emotional honesty leaps off every page—here is a woman who is not afraid to show herself, warts and all. In admitting her vulnerabilities, she makes it okay for us to be just who we are too.

In an interview, she was asked about her relationship to money. As a single mother living off her writing, her financial security has been precarious at best. She spoke of having survived, at times, off the generosity of friends, and then said something that leaped out at me. "I know that if I feel any deprivation or fear [about money], the solution is to give. The solution is to go find some mothers on the streets of San Raphael and give them tens and twenties and mail off another $50 to Doctors Without Borders to use for the refugees in Kosovo. Because I know that giving is the way we can feel abundant. Giving is the way that we fill ourselves up. . . . For me the way to fill up is through service and sharing and getting myself to give more than I feel comfortable giving."

To me, a person who has a great deal of fear when it comes to money, the thought of giving money away precisely when I felt like clinging to it seemed terrifying. Sick of constantly being fearful about money, I decided to give it a try. Amazingly, it really works. I feel less afraid the more I give.

It's a paradox. If we are afraid of not having enough, we think we need to hold on tightly to what we have and work hard to get more. As Anne Lamott and I found out, that perspective only makes us more afraid, because we get caught in a cycle of clinging and hoarding. When is enough enough? Is $5,000 enough? $50,000? $100,000? $1 million? A recent study found that no matter how much money people made, they thought they would be happier if only they had more. Whether they made $20,000 a year or $200,000, everyone thought they needed a bit more.

If we turn around and give instead of hoarding everything, we suddenly experience the abundance we do have. Most of us, particularly those of us living in Western societies, have a great deal, and when we share what we have, we feel our abundance. It becomes real to us, and that diminishes our fears. I read about a woman who was suffering from depression and contemplating suicide because of back pain and poverty. She found a kid foraging in the Dumpster and thought to herself, "I don't have a lot, but at least I can fix this kid a peanut butter sandwich." Giving away that peanut butter sandwich reminded her of the abundance she still had, even in the projects. If she could still give, her life wasn't so bleak after all. She now runs a volunteer program in Dallas that feeds hundreds of kids a day. It started from that one day when she gave away the sandwich.

Giving Helps Us Experience Our Connection with Others

*Just as the wave cannot exist for itself, but is ever
a part of the heaving surface of the ocean, so must I never
live my life for itself, but always in the experience
which is going on all around me.*

—ALBERT SCHWEITZER

My friend Tom recently went to his high school reunion and had a surprising experience. "I always thought reunions were stupid," he said, "and so I never went. But an old friend called and guilt-tripped me into it, so I went. It was strange, but not in the way I had imagined.

"I'm a very successful financial analyst, a bit on the driven side, but it got me all the things I thought I wanted—a great condo in the city, a country house, fancy car. So I showed up with a bit of a self-satisfied attitude. There were plenty of surprises, both in appearances—people change a lot in twenty years—and in what individuals had done with their lives. The biggest surprise was that the people who seemed the most happy were not those who had 'made it' in the sense that I would have understood. There were a number of people in my income bracket—lawyers, computer guys—but for the most part they were the most unhappy and lonely.

"The interaction that really affected me was with an old girlfriend who was a nursery school teacher. When she talked about 'her kids,' her eyes would light up with a kind of excitement and energy I hadn't seen for years.

"It came to me that she had a very deep connection to the people in her work life—kids, parents, and other teachers—that came out of her giving them her time, energy, and enthusiasm, whereas I had all the trimmings of a great life but wasn't connected to anything at all except my wallet. That was the beginning of my midlife crisis, and it hasn't been easy. I decided to take a small step and become a Big Brother to a twelve-year-old kid from the projects. I've been really enjoying myself, taking him to ball games and helping with homework."

The wonderful thing about giving is that you can't help but experience a good feeling when you do it. Humans are social creatures. We're made to live within the company of others, and initiating that connection—making it concrete—just feels good in and of itself. When we get narrowly focused on just ourselves, we lose track of the sense of connection to others that helping gives us and instead experience isolation and loneliness. Far too many of us are stuck in that state today. Cut off from enough meaningful contact, we drift alone in the universe. No matter our circumstances, we can always experience human connection simply by reaching out to help someone else. When it comes to connecting, what you give is what you'll get.

Giving Allows Us to Look Deeply at Ourselves

*Just as we are, we are giving and receiving life.
But we miss this because we are caught up with all of the
efforts to be right, to be the best, to be the winner, to be first. All
the evaluations and judgments we make about ourselves
and others separate us from this simple being.*

—ROBERT JOSHIN ALTHOUSE SENSEI

For three years, I delivered dinner once a week to people with AIDS. I would go to the distribution point, pick up ten or fifteen packaged meals, get a piece of paper that showed me the addresses of where to go, and set off. For three years I watched my reactions to the very simple act of delivering food, and I learned a lot about myself.

People with chronic illnesses tend to be worse off financially, and it was certainly true of the folks on my route. I was required to drive in the "worst" part of town, and it was usually dark when I made my rounds. My first reaction was fear. After a few weeks, I became somewhat comfortable, and the fear mostly receded into the background. Sometimes if I were walking down the long, dark corridor of a welfare hotel, I would fear the thought of someone grabbing me, raping me, and infecting me with AIDS.

Most of the time, what I felt was pride. Wasn't I a "good" person to be doing such a thing? Wasn't I brave, generous, even saintly? Every time I delivered the meals, I had a story line about my virtuous behavior running in my head. I was so caught up with myself that on more than one occasion, I missed a chance to be truly helpful because I was so caught up in either my fear or my grandiose thoughts.

My goal with this story is to point out that giving triggers all kinds of thoughts and feelings. Examining them can be useful in our personal development—we learn more if we adopt an "Oh, isn't that interesting," approach to what we discover instead of bludgeoning ourselves with "Aren't I terrible?" My experience with the meals showed me how much I want to look good—especially to myself.

What should you do with what you discover about yourself? Acknowledge it—you really need to think of yourself as a good person. Have compassion for it. Don't try to fix or change it. Just hold the truth in the spaciousness of your being. By accepting it instead of denying it, pushing it away, trying to make it be different, or forcing yourself into some other position, you create the space for it to transform. Even if it never changes, at least you are aware of it and you're being

Generosity Helps Us See There Is No Difference Between Giving and Receiving

*Each day as we embrace the sun with love and joy,
we can come to the realization that giving and receiving
are the same. Therefore, we will give equally
without reservation.*

—AEESHA ABABIO-CLOTTEY AND KOKOMON CLOTTEY

In the book *Beyond Fear*, social worker Aeesha Ababio-Clottey tells this story. Every day, on her way to and from work, she passed the same homeless person begging at the entrance to the subway. Rushing past, she would never even look at him, much less put a penny in his cup. One evening, she was a dime short for the ticket that would get her home. "I looked around," she wrote, "and everyone was in a hurry, trying to get home.... And as I looked, people avoided eye contact, with the unspoken message: Don't ask me!"

Finally, in her desperation, she turned to the beggar and asked to borrow a dime. He insisted she take a quarter. Then she inquired if he had a place to live and told him about the treatment center where she worked and how she could help him. "I'm quite happy, thank you," he replied. "I meet all kinds of people here, and I really enjoy myself and I don't want to change it."

What a morality play! The professional "giver," the social worker, has ignored the professional "receiver," the beggar, for months. Then she ends up having to receive from him, and discovers that while he has no use for what she has to give, he has what she needs.

It's easy in the giving position to assume a sense of superiority—I, in my benevolence, will assist you, you poor thing. This creates all kinds of problems: The receiver can fall into a sense of inferiority and dependence that often creates anger and resentment, while the giver develops an inflated ego and a false sense of independence. When we remember that at any given moment we might be in need of help, though, we can then offer our services on a more equal level.

As we open our hearts, we come to see that there is really no difference between giving and receiving. They are just two sides of the experience because neither can exist without the other. It is like imagining breathing without both the inhaling (receiving) and the exhaling (giving). Perhaps if we had a word for the experience of giving that encompasses both aspects, we would see it for what it truly is—one act with two parts, both honorable, both crucial.

Giving fills Us
Like Getting Cannot

*For many years, I was a man riding an ox,
looking for an ox to ride on.*

—Meister Eckhart

I once was talking about the nature of addiction with an acquaintance who is, by her definition, a food addict. She said that she overate because she felt there was a hole in the center of her being. "The difference between me and you, Mary Jane," she said, "is that you know the hole can't be filled and I keep thinking it can be filled with food."

For me, this was one of those remarks that comes with lights around it: Pay attention, this is important. I've thought a lot about that hole over the years, and I am convinced that most of us have this sense of emptiness. We spend our lives trying to fill the hole with money, prestige, power, or even material objects. We think that if we get enough stuff, the hole will be filled and our desire will be satiated.

This approach is not surprising, considering we live in a culture that survives on our consumerism. The economy booms when sales surge because we're throwing our money around; the economy falters when sales drop because we rein ourselves in. Every single day, on the radio, TV, the Internet, billboards, and in magazines and newspapers, we are encouraged and enticed to buy, buy, buy. Brilliant people create very sophisticated ads to convince us that if only we had this car, this computer, this Internet server, this toothpaste, or this brand of soap, we would be happy and fulfilled. It's only natural that we are focused on getting the red Porsche, the 4,000-square foot house, or the Ben & Jerry's ice cream.

Our desire will never disappear, because stuff can't fill the hole, no matter how much we get. Books and magazines are always filled with stories of folks who "had it all" and yet were miserable. Our desires may change—we get the beautiful girl, the horse, or the million dollars in the bank, so now we want more friends, a child, or a vacation home—but they don't go away because desire is a natural part of the human condition. The problem isn't with our desire but, like the reasoning of my friend the overeater, in thinking that the things we desire will fill the hole.

The answer is found in giving, not getting. If we tap into the natural sense of abundance that exists in each of us instead of focusing on filling the hole, we will be filled. It's a paradox—by focusing on getting, we remain forever empty; by focusing on giving, we become full.

This idea is hard to accept because it goes against our cultural upbringing. I know that part of me is still convinced that the hole is not filled because I just haven't gotten the right things. If I did, this part says, then I would be happy.

As I have both gotten more and given more, I've realized that generosity is the true creator of happiness and peace of mind. As the Buddhist teacher Jack Kornfield once said, "Do you know any really generous people who aren't happy?" The real way to discover this truth, however, is to try it yourself. Try opening your heart and giving, particularly when you feel the hole in the center of your being. Magically it disappears, at least for a little while, as the love from your heart pours into it, and into the world.

Giving Allows Us to Offer Our Unique Gifts

Every person born in this world represents
something new, something that never existed before,
something original and unique.

—MARTIN BUBER

The ancient Greeks and Romans believed each human was born with a tutelary, or guardian, spirit inside of us, a being that embodied our true essence. It was our task in life to set this spirit free so that our unique gifts could become manifest. The Greeks called this being a person's *daemon*, the Romans called it the *genius* (from the same Latin root as generosity—*genere*, which means to beget or produce.) Socrates, for example, was believed to have a daemon who would speak up if he was about to do something that went counter to his essence. In Rome, it was customary to offer a sacrifice to your genius on your birthday, not to only receive gifts for yourself on that day but to give something to your guiding spirit. According to their beliefs, this being comes to us when we are born and it carries the fullness of our undeveloped potential. If you cultivate your gifts, the genius will become a household god when you die. If you ignore your potential, it will turn into a larva upon your death, a ghost that preys on the living.

These ancient beliefs match my own—we each are born with unique gifts to offer the world (*genius* is a synonym for *gift*), and our task in life is to discover our gifts and actualize them. This task is like a hero's journey more than any kind of small feat. As Marianne Williamson once said, "It takes more courage sometimes to face our greatness than it does to face our weakness."

In our culture, we are not taught how to recognize our gifts, much less manifest them. We are taught to have goals—graduate from high school, go to college, get married, raise a family—but not how to discover our unique purpose. Who in our childhood encouraged us to answer the questions: What do you love? What are you here to give? Even as adults, many of us have trouble even recognizing our unique talents and abilities. Often when I ask people to name their gifts, they look at me blankly.

Like the Greeks and Romans, I believe that discovering these gifts is the task of our lifetime. Through our generosity, we can begin to see the shadow of our unique genius and offer it to the world. The nature of a gift is that it demands to be given. If we keep it to ourselves and fail to offer it to others, it dies unfulfilled.

Think back to what the Romans believed. If we release our gifts, then we will have succeeded in our life's purpose and the genius (our self) will become a god. If however, we fail to release our gifts, we will become hungry ghosts, harassing the living forever. Perhaps our ghosts harass the living because we are finally trying to give, but can't because we are dead. While we're alive, though, it is never too late to share these gifts. What makes you feel most alive when you are sharing it? Figuring this out will lead you to your particular gifts and your purpose for being alive.

Generosity Connects Us to Nature

Consider, too, the generous gifts of the natural world:
beauty, protection, abundance, and resources from trees, plants,
flowers, and the animals that share our fragile planet.

—KAY CHORAO

Although I'm originally from New England, I've lived in California for twenty-five years. Every year, I am still surprised by spring arriving in February. You'd think I would have reset my internal clock by now, but each February, when the plum trees burst into fuchsia hues, the daffodils push out their sunny heads, and the quince bushes show their salmon flowers, I am amazed.

Today, I took a break from writing to walk around my neighborhood and revel in spring. With the topic of generosity on my mind, I couldn't help but notice how bountiful and generous nature is. The blossoms on the plum tree are profuse, in excess of what is needed to produce fruit. The fruit in the summer will be bountiful; a few years ago a plum tree I had was so laden with fruit that a branch broke off from the sheer weight. My family and everyone in my office feasted on plums for weeks and weeks.

37

The life-force is inherently generous—in the wealth of different life forms as well as the profusion of blossoms, fruit, and seed—and all these forms depend on one another. The rabbit eats the flowers, the mountain lion eats the rabbit, when the lion dies it becomes compost that fertilizes the tree that produces the flower, and on and on. Every player in the cycle literally lives off the others, with only the sun outside the process—giving but not receiving.

We are a part of this cycle, and our generosity is simply part of the great wheel of life. Our whole life can be viewed as a continuous cycle of transaction. We receive bounty from others—love, wisdom, lessons, and support as well as food, clothing, and shelter. After pausing to appreciate what we've been given and perhaps polishing those gifts that are slightly tarnished, we pass them on to other recipients. This is the essence of the web of life. All of creation, from the tiniest particle to the greatest mountain, is involved in this generous and continual exchange of energy.

When we give, we take our place in the order of things and we experience our deep connection to all of nature. Giving is natural; we don't have to hoard it. In this cycle, it's as though we are standing in a giant line, receiving with one hand and passing what we received on to the next. Thus, giving—of ourselves and our resources—is a profound reminder that we are not separate from the natural world but an integral and responsible part of it.

Giving Allows Us to Experience Oneness

Constantly remind yourself, "I am a member of the whole body of conscious things." If you think of yourself as a mere "part," then love for humanity will not well up in your heart; you will look for some reward in every act of kindness and miss the boon which the act itself is offering. Then all your work will be seen as mere duty and not as the very porthole connecting you with the Universe itself.

—Marcus Aurelius

I was speaking in a classroom of third-graders one day about kindness and generosity. I asked the kids why we should do nice things for one another. Hands popped up: "Because it's the right thing to do." "Because it makes the other person feel good." "Because then they'll be nice to you." Then a girl in the corner said, "Because when you share with people it makes you bigger, and when you don't share it makes you smaller."

This child articulated something that even many adults never get. Giving makes us bigger. What I think she meant by bigger is that the very act of giving makes real the truth about life that mystics, sages, and even certain scientists are trying to get us to understand—we are completely interconnected. Not really separate, even though it seems as though we are.

On one level, we are indeed each private, individual selves, making our way through life as best we can. In that realm, we are small. Even on this level, we can see the effects of our good deeds—a person who would otherwise go hungry is fed; a lost child is returned to her family; a forest is preserved.

At some other level, the non-material level, there is no separation between me and the hungry person, me and the lost girl, or me and the trees. We are all, as Marcus Aurelius puts it, aspects of the vast body of consciousness that is life itself. On this level, we are huge.

This truth is beyond the realm of our ordinary experience and is often difficult to talk about. Many people talk in generalities about oneness and lack of separation. I believe that such lack of separateness has to be experienced to be understood, which is why the practice of generosity is so important. The more we live out of our generosity, the more we experience this larger self. Being more aware of our oneness will eventually help us make wiser decisions about life.

Generosity Helps Us Glimpse the Truth About Life

We live in a universe where relationships are primary. . . .
Nothing exists independent of its relationships. We are con-
stantly creating the world—evoking it from many potentials—
as we participate in all its many interactions.

—MARGARET J. WHEATLEY

*f*or centuries, we lived with the model that the world is a machine, and if we don't expend a great deal of energy keeping it and ourselves going in an orderly fashion, it will run down like a clock that has not been wound. According to theorist Margaret J. Wheatley, this view is of a universe, "that cannot be trusted with its own processes for growth and rejuvenation."

Beginning in the twentieth century, however, scientists began to discover that this view of the world was wrong. These scientists have begun to understand that life is inherently orderly and that it is in a constant process of creating and renewing itself. Everything alive is a living system, inextricably growing and changing inside a vast self-renewing living system of life itself.

This awareness of how life actually works has tremendous implications for all aspects of human endeavors—everything from how businesses should be organized to how we can relate to one another personally. Because this worldview is only a hundred years old, we have just begun to incorporate the truth of it into our lives.

Generosity has a tremendous role in this new worldview. The practice of generosity allows people to experience the ways life really works: Nothing exists alone, but only in relationship, and the future is not pre-ordained but is brought about through the creation of relationships. When we reach out to others, for instance, we actually create the future through our giving and our interaction.

Think about it this way: You are a schoolteacher longing to make a difference for students who are having a hard time learning to read through conventional methods. One day you go to a party, even though you don't really feel like going. At the party, you meet a man, a computer programmer, who is also yearning to have more of an impact on the world. You and he have an intense conversation about your ideas for teaching reading. You two really connect on this idea and meet several other times; finally, you work together to create a revolutionary new literacy Web site that really takes off, helping thousands of kids learn to read. If you hadn't talked to that man at the party, the Web site would never have been born and many kids would have stayed functionally illiterate. Your interaction with him, however, resulted in that Web site, and, in a small way, you helped determine a brighter future for certain students.

Generosity is all about relationships, about creating and enacting connections, and about trusting that what goes around, comes around. The more you experience generosity, the more you will experience how the good you do comes back to you in some form or another.

3

The Spirit of Giving

There must be more to life than having everything!

—MAURICE SENDAK

This chapter explores the attitudes that cultivate the openheartedness that is found in a giving heart. For some of us, such attitudes are innate, or they were taught to us when we were so young that they seem second nature now. For others of us, these attitudes may require some rethinking of our fundamental assumptions about life. Attitudes support behavior—we behave in certain ways because we believe certain things. If we change our minds, we can change our lives. All it takes is a willingness to change. It's a matter of figuring out what brings us true contentment—whether it's believing that there isn't enough to go around and we must hold on tight to what we have and look for more; or whether it's trusting that as we open our hearts to ourselves and others we will be constantly replenished with love and the sense of fulfillment that comes only from sharing our gifts.

We Are Inherently Generous

Let's share.

—ANA LI, AGE THREE

My daughter Ana Li wanted potato chips for breakfast this morning (I'm not too strict when it comes to food). She took four chips, then gave me one of her four. "Let's share," she said. Whenever she eats something, she always gives me part of it, whether I want it or not.

Flash to the afternoon. We've been to the store and she's climbing back in her car seat. She hates being strapped in, so the car seat is public enemy number 1. She balks and jumps up and down on the seat. When I say, "Ana, please sit down because someone is waiting for this parking space," she turns, sees the car, and instantly sits. This isn't unusual either; she quickly gets into her seat whenever someone is waiting.

I've thought a lot about the meaning of these behaviors. Conventional child-rearing wisdom says that kids are inherently possessive and self-centered, and that they need to be taught to share and to be considerate to others. I've learned from my experience that children, just as adults, can have feelings of "Mine, you can't have it," and "I want you to also enjoy this thing that I have," or feelings of "I want it exactly my way," and "What's good for you?" Selfishness and consideration exist in all of us. They are natural tendencies, two sides of the human coin. (Even scientists admit that humans developed both self-serving behavior and a genuine desire to help others because groups whose members helped one another survived better than groups whose members did not.)

If both behaviors exist within us, it is inaccurate to say that we need to learn to be generous. We already possess generosity. It's like a river that is always flowing within us. To enter the stream more readily, we need to peel away the dams to generosity that we have built up over our lives. We need to abandon the blocks we thought would keep us from feeling our own pain and the pain of others. We need to get rid of the attitudes that have reinforced our possessive aspects, so that the stream of generosity in our hearts can break free. The more we uncover the blocks, the more our generosity will gurgle and rush.

Giving Is Easy When We Go with the Grain

It doesn't matter how long we may have been stuck
in a sense of our limitations. If we go into a darkened room
and turn on the light, it doesn't matter if the room has been dark
for a day, a week, or ten thousand years—we turn on the light
and it is illumined. Once we contact our capacity for love
and happiness . . . the light has been turned on.

—SHARON SALZBERG

The state of affairs can often get you down. It's easy to become overwhelmed by all that needs fixing. It's equally easy to slip into despair, believing that since one person can't make a difference, it's not worth trying. However, there are many stories about people who decided to do something that was important to them, and who ended up having a huge impact. Think about the woman who started Mothers Against Drunk Drivers (MADD), for example, after her daughter was killed by a drunk driver. Since MADD's inception, drunk driving has declined every year. There's also four-year-old Isis Johnson, who asked her grandmother one day, "Can we send the chicken we have left to the children in Ethiopia?" With that question, she and her grandmother founded the Isis Johnson Foundation, which collects food and clothing for needy Louisianans.

The question for each of us is this: Where does your river of generosity naturally emerge? What is yours to give? Is it advice? Money? Time? Inspiring others to take action?

We each are born with a spark of life that is uniquely our own. We're here to find ways to express that spark, and when we can express it, giving is natural. It doesn't feel like work because you are going with the grain of your being, not against it.

My husband Don expresses his spark through plants. He can work in the garden happily for hours. He's free with plant advice for anyone that asks, and loves to give plants away. He'd be a natural for helping to create a community garden, something he loves more than coaching little league sports. You also have a spark of life that, when tapped, gives you all kinds of energy and enthusiasm. The world needs that from you. If you aren't inclined to work with troubled adolescents, don't volunteer for it, even if the folks from your church are asking you to. If a particular activity doesn't speak to your soul, you'll be stuck in obligation and guilt, which are killers of the giving heart. Instead, find something you truly are enthusiastic about and express your giving in that way.

Every one of us needs opportunities to express our generosity, but they will be different for each of us. There is no one right way. By sticking with what feels natural to you, you will be more inclined to keep giving.

51

To Give Is to Live

*What do we live for, if it is not to make
life less difficult for each other?*

—George Eliot

I once read an Indian parable by Eknath Easwaran about a man who always lived the letter of the law and was a model of respectability. When he died, he was sent to Chitragupta, the cosmic accountant who keeps the ledger on all human beings. Chitragupta looked up the man's name in the black book and found nothing. Nothing in the credit column, nothing in the debit column. Chitragupta didn't know what to do. He'd never encountered such a situation before. Here was a man who "had never helped anybody, never hurt anybody, never offended anybody, never loved anybody," writes Easwaran. "He couldn't be sent to heaven, but he couldn't be sent to hell either."

Chitragupta went to the god of creation, Brahma, figuring that since Brahma made the man, Brahma would know what to do. But Brahma, after studying all the heavenly statutes, couldn't figure out what to do with the guy either. "Take him to Krishna," he suggested. "Let him decide."

Krishna was determined to find a solution. He carefully examined the man's records again and saw, in almost invisible pencil, one entry in the credit column: "When six, gave two cents to a beggar." Now Krishna had the answer. "Give the man back his two cents and send him back to Earth to try again."

Krishna's response shows the importance of giving. Under a strict accounting, the guy should have been let into heaven because he had one item in the credit column and no debits. The great Krishna, however, reasoned that one good deed is not enough, and the man was sent back to try again.

The nature of human life shows that we do both good and harm. It's impossible to go without helping or hurting others during the course of our lives, which is why the gods were stumped by a person who seemed to have done neither. We will, in the course of our lives, harm other beings, but until we have learned to give freely of ourselves, we have not truly learned how to live.

53

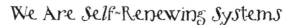

We Are Self-Renewing Systems

Life is constantly providing us with new funds,
new resources, even when we are reduced to immobility.
In life's ledger there is no such thing as frozen assets.

—Henry Miller

I have a friend whose father is a fisherman. Fishing has always been a hard vocation, and recently it has been very difficult to make a living because of over-fishing. My friend's father is bitter and angry—at the government and at the other countries who have sent their huge boats just outside U.S. waters and depleted the fish population. He won't even entertain the possibility of doing something different with his life, even though he is quite talented with his hands. He just wants someone to fix the situation so he can go back to the way he was. Not coincidentally, he is one of the stingiest people I have ever met.

We often hold back on our generosity because we are afraid of running out—of money, of time, of ideas. This fear makes us think we need to cling to the way it was. We believe that "you can't teach an old dog new tricks," and we don't trust our capacity to renew ourselves or our ability to learn.

Living from a giving heart means knowing that each

of us is a living system and that living systems are constantly learning and changing. With this view, how can you be afraid to give something away? You trust in your capacity to transform with the changing situation and to generate more, and you know that whatever you give will come back to you in another form.

This is not an easy lesson for many of us. We have to let go of old mechanistic models of the world and trust in our capacity for regeneration. We are living in times where old ways of doing things are dying at a rapid rate and where we need to continually remake ourselves. My field—book publishing—has changed dramatically over the past five years, and I have had to change as well. Chances are you have, too.

Even though I know that I am capable of learning, of growing and changing, I find myself sometimes sliding back into the old ways of thinking. Posting the quote by Henry Miller on my computer is one way I've found to bring myself back into my new ways of thinking. When I find myself scared and withholding, I also tell myself, "I'm intelligent and resourceful. I'm sure I can figure something out."

When we trust in our capacity to generate and regenerate, we can be our generous selves more fully.

Generosity Comes in Many forms

A gift consists not in what is done or given,
but in the intention of the giver or doer.

—SENECA

In his spiritual autobiography, Gandhi talks about his shortcomings as a parent, particularly about not giving his sons enough of an academic education because he was more concerned with a moral one. His oldest son, he wrote, "has often given vent to his distress privately before me and publicly in the press; the other sons have generously forgiven the failure as unavoidable."

His words leaped out at me—I'd never thought of forgiveness as a generous act. Like any other generous act, though, it requires moving away from your self-focused perspective and making an overture to another. Forgiveness is particularly generous because it requires putting aside your own legitimate hurts in order to reestablish a new bond.

We tend to think of generosity in terms of money. Gandhi reminds us that there are many ways to be generous in our very being. We can give time, care, thanks, advice, and joy. We can give support or respectful distance. We can be generous listeners. We can be generous with our words, our touch, or our looks. We can be generous with our ideas, our creativity, or our knowledge. We can be generous with our possessions and our compassion. We can even be generous with our forgiveness.

My tenant Kathy jumps to mind when I think of the forms of generosity. She is so free with her enthusiasm, it is infectious. Bubbly, warm, and caring, she can jolly almost anyone out of a bad mood. She's always ready to volunteer for any project around the house. Need help moving rocks? Kathy volunteers. Need someone to go to the dump? She's ready to jump into action. Even though she embodies generosity to me, I doubt that she would characterize herself as generous, because we haven't been trained to think of our human qualities as reflecting generosity. Yet her essence, her very being, is a great gift to my family.

Where are you generous? Are you quick to forgive? Able to listen well? Know just when to offer a hug or a comforting hand on the shoulder? Full of ideas that you share freely? If our intention is to give from the abundance we feel, we are being generous, in whatever form we offer it. By narrowing our thinking about generosity, we deprive ourselves of a myriad of ways to live from our giving hearts, and we neglect to recognize the gifts we are offering on a daily basis by our very being.

57

We Can Make a Difference

Even the most hard-nose physicist is beginning to
admit that the flap of a butterfly's wins can change the weather
thousands of miles away. Everything we do matters.

—GLORIA STEINEM

I was driving down the street one hot, dry, windy fall day, the most dangerous time of the year in California for fires. Looking uphill, I saw that a small fire had broken out in the tinder-dry grass between the street and a row of houses above me. Quickly I looked about for a phone and saw a small gas station up ahead. It was one of those tiny boxes with a person inside who takes your money and pushes a button to release the gas pump. I screeched up to the station and jumped out. No pay phone. I ran to the box, where a bored teenager sat inside. "Excuse me," I said, "I've just seen a grassfire starting. Can I use your phone to call 911?"

"No," he said.

"Well, can you call 911 for me?" I asked.

"No," he responded. "It's not my problem."

Incredulous, I decided not to argue with him and raced off to find another phone.

Years ago, when the concept of self-esteem was all the rage, a professor in childhood development said to me, "You know, feeling good about yourself is important, but it's only a piece of what kids need. In addition to self-esteem, they need self-efficacy—the sense that they can take an action in the world and it will have an effect. So many kids, especially adolescents, feel that nothing they can do will make any difference, so why bother? They have never been taught that everything we do matters."

It was the first time I heard of self-efficacy, but it made a lot of sense to me. Like any other attribute, it becomes second nature if you practice it. If you call when you see a fire, the fire engines will come and the fire will be put out quickly so that property and lives can be saved. Self-efficacy breeds action—if what I do can have an effect, somewhere, for someone, then I'm more inclined to do something.

While I know that there are people in the world like the kid who wouldn't call 911 for me, I think most of us have some sense of self-efficacy and some belief in our ability to have an effect. The complexity of the problems that surround us makes it easy to lose faith in our efficacy or fall into despair.

When I begin to doubt my efficacy, I try two things. I sit a bit with my feelings of despair and really acknowledge the difficulty of what I am facing. Once I

Whatever We Do,
We Do for Ourselves

*The gift is to the giver, and comes back
most to him—it cannot fail.*

—WALT WHITMAN

While writing this book, I heard the following story twice, which I took to be a definite sign that I was meant to use it here. It goes like this: There was a farmer who was the premier corn grower in his community. His corn was always sweeter and better than anyone else's, and it always won the blue ribbon at the county fair. At the end of the growing season, he would take his seed corn, the corn that would be sown the following spring, and gave a large portion of it to all the farmers in the area. "Why do you do that?" someone asked him. "Don't you want to keep the best corn for yourself?"

"I do it for myself," replied the farmer. "My corn will be cross-pollinated by bees and wind from the other fields, and if they have inferior corn, mine will soon become inferior as well."

That farmer really understood that the world is so interconnected that whatever we do for someone else we are also doing for ourselves. No action can be taken in isolation, because everything we do ripples out and has some kind of effect. The bad we do generates more bad—just think of all the places in the world caught up in religious or tribal feuds. Group A kills members of Group B and the hatred generated from that act fuels Group B's killing of folks from Group A, and on and on down through the generations.

The ripple effect is true for good deeds as well, it's just less visible. Often, it is merely just that the bad things quit happening. The kid you help by becoming a Big Brother or Sister doesn't end up robbing you or raping your little sister. The person you tutor in reading is able to be a productive member of society rather than someone supported by welfare. The people you provided with a loan so they could set up a business exporting products from the rainforest in Brazil do not have to participate in killing the rainforest, a small step toward preserving our planet from destruction.

When we truly understand this interdependence, we also understand that whatever we do, we do for ourselves. As Dr. Martin Luther King, Jr., once said, "We may have all come on different ships, but we are all in the same boat now." And a mighty small boat it is.

Gratitude and Generosity Are Indivisible

As I express my gratitude, I become more aware of it.
And the greater my awareness, the greater my need to express it.
What happens here is a spiraling ascent, a process of growth
in ever-expanding circles around a steady center.

—BROTHER DAVID STEINDL-RAST

Years ago, my friend Grace got into a financial jam. She bought a one-bedroom condo in the boom years of the '80s, and then watched as the market for condos dropped like a rock. Then she was transferred to another state and couldn't get rid of it because she owed more on the mortgage than she could sell it for. She couldn't just walk away from it, because the bank could repossess the house she and her husband managed to buy despite the condo. So she rented it out, but the huge mortgage continued to be an albatross around her neck. Over the years, all of us close to Grace, including her friend Molly, have heard her express anxiety about the condo, especially whenever a tenant left.

Molly recently called up Grace to tell her that she and her husband had just made a killing because his Internet company went public, and that she was going to give Grace the money to pay off the mortgage on the condo. Grace was overwhelmed. "You can't do that," she said. "It's so much money." Molly replied, "I feel so grateful that my life has been so blessed. I just want to spread some of the blessings around. I've heard you complain about that condo for years. It would be give me great joy to alleviate your burden." Grace kept demurring, but Molly persisted, and finally Grace accepted. As a consequence, Molly got to feel the delicious sensation of giving a huge gift to someone she loved.

Not only was Grace relieved of the burden of the condo, she also got to experience a sense of gratitude that spread to all aspects of her life. When telling me this story the other day, she said, "You know, I have been blessed with truly generous friends all my life. Molly ended up giving me more than I needed to pay off the loan. What I would really like to do now is to use the rest of the money to help my in-laws get out of debt."

Both Molly and Grace have entered the ever-expanding circle of openheartedness that comes from the interplay of generosity and gratitude. It doesn't matter where you enter the circle—in gratitude or with generosity. The more you experience one, the more the other enhances your life as well. You feel truly grateful, and from that fullness you offer something to someone else—an encouraging word, or a helping hand. In return, you receive love, the feeling of connection, and a sense of satisfaction and fulfillment that continues to fuel your gratitude for the gifts of life you have received.

Few of us will ever be as extravagant in our giving as Molly, but that doesn't matter. This beautiful circle of giving and thankfulness occurs regardless of the size or the form of the gift.

We Are Both Generous and Withholding

Complete possession is proved only by giving.
All you are unable to give possesses you.

—ANDRE GIDE

I have a friend who is one of the all-time great givers of emotional support. If you are upset, she is right there. She calls, and will spend as long as you need talking about whatever's troubling you. She offers empathy and insight. She'll hold you in her awareness throughout the day and will check in ten times if that's what you need. When it comes to being a caring friend in a crisis, her generosity knows no bounds. Even though she's materially well off, I have never received a gift from her or been taken out to lunch. She's just not generous when it comes to material things.

We are all generous to greater or lesser degrees, and we are all generous in different realms. We've learned to be openhearted in some areas, but not in others. It's good to take stock of just where and when we are and aren't generous. Once we become conscious of our habits, we have more freedom to change them, if we desire.

When I ask myself where am I generous, I realize

that I offer my time and home to those I care about. I am also generous with my problem-solving abilities and my wisdom about how life seems to work. I also realize that I am especially stingy with money and sometimes stingy with praise, encouragement, or words of love, particularly with those I am close to.

My money stinginess makes sense to me. I am afraid of not having enough, so I hold back my generosity. I'm not afraid of running out of empathy or insight, so I give freely of those things. If I think deeply about Andre Gide's quote, I see that my stinginess with money is a problem. In a certain sense, money does possess me. I spend a great deal of time worrying about how to get it and how to keep it, while the people I know who are generous with money, regardless of how much they have, are not obsessed by it.

My stinginess with verbal support comes, I think, from my fear that I will have to give everything in a relationship while the other person does nothing. The problem here is that my verbal stinginess virtually ensures that the other person will not want to give me the love and nurturing I want. Love is a cycle that grows in a mutual atmosphere of freely given and received care and concern.

Where are you generous and where are you stingy?

We Can Unblock Our Giving

In the long run, we get no more than we have been willing to risk giving.

—SHELDON KOPP

A few years ago, I was in the produce market and, in the middle of the lettuce aisle, saw a large bin of sweet peas for sale. They are one of my favorite flowers so I picked a bunch and held them up to my nose. A woman passing by commented on how beautiful they were and asked me how much they cost. "Two dollars," I proclaimed. "Would you like a bunch?" "Oh," she said, hesitating, "I'd better not. I'm watching my budget." She then turned and walked away. How sad, I thought, she obviously wanted them but wasn't able to spend the $2. So I picked out a bunch, went to the checkout stand, paid for them, and then found her in a different aisle. "Here," I said, "I want you to have these." She wouldn't take them, and I left feeling frustrated and embarrassed. I had wanted to give someone a treat but my giving was blocked. I've never tried to do such a thing again.

We all have reasons why we hold ourselves back from giving. Perhaps we tried in the past and were unsuccessful, so we've learned to limit that impulse. As a child, perhaps we got in trouble for giving our toys

69

away to friends, or got burned out in young adulthood because of a volunteer position we took on. Maybe we're angry that we haven't gotten what we think we deserve in life, so we resent the thought of anyone else having something. Perhaps we're so busy we can't even see our own needs, much less anyone else's. We could also hold certain self-protecting ideas like "It's a dog-eat-dog world" because we are covering up some deep hurt we experienced when young, one that now keeps us from reaching out.

These reasons deserve some examination because they are the bricks in the dam that is holding back the flow of giving in your life. As long as they remain as solid and hard as they are now, you will limit the experience of joy that giving can bring to you.

I'm not suggesting that you dynamite the dam. These bricks have served some good purpose for you. They have protected you from some hurt that you had no other way to deal with at the time. All I'm suggesting is that you reexamine them now and determine whether they are still necessary. The first step is "seeing clearly how we hold back, how we pull away, how we shut down, how we close off, and then learning how to open," as Buddhist teacher Pema Chödrön puts it.

Why do you hold yourself back from giving as

much as you can? Gently ask the question and gently receive the answer. The most important place to express your generosity in this moment is toward yourself and for all you have endured that has caused your heart to close in the first place.

You Can't Say Yes if You Can't Say No

We need to respectfully pay attention to ourselves, tuning in when the little voice inside wants to say 'no.'

—SUE PATTON THOELE

My friend Monica just spent some time at a Zen retreat center, where she was asked to correspond with a male prisoner who had written looking for a Buddhist pen pal. She didn't want to, but felt she should, so she agreed to write. She did say that she would prefer writing to a woman, but was told that there were no women in the pile.

It's been a month now. Every day she says she should write that letter, and every day she doesn't. Every day she feels guilty—a "good" person would have already written the letter—and feels resentful that she was roped into the situation in the first place.

Monica's problem is familiar to many of us, particularly women: She can't say no. As I told my husband when I first met him, if you can't say no, you can't say yes. That's because in order to truly say yes to something, it has to be wholehearted. You have to really mean it, and you can't really mean it if you don't feel free to say no, especially if that's what is true for you.

People who have trouble saying no take on too much and end up bitter and burned out. They are the women who bake the cookies for every classroom event, drive all the kids in the neighborhood to the movies every weekend, singlehandedly take on the new project at work—all while tending to their dying parent. At the very least, they are exhausted, but most likely they are prone to feelings of martyrdom: they're holding up the whole world while the rest of us are just loafing around. Maybe they have twenty-five people angry with them because they couldn't possibly meet all their commitments and they feel victimized by the other people's anger; after all, they are trying so hard and doing so much!

This kind of giving is not giving at all. It is a compulsion that usually comes from a lack of self-worth. They are so afraid of the disapproval of the person making the request that they must say yes. As a result, they have never experienced true generosity, which comes from an overflow of a sense of caring, not compulsion.

73

Even if we don't suffer from low self-esteem, it can be hard to disappoint someone who is making a direct request of us. But unless we begin to truly listen for our "no's," our "yeses," like Monica's, will be half-hearted at best and a true burden at worst.

True Giving Means Letting Go of Control

Blessed are those who can give without remembering.

—ELIZABETH BIBESCO

I have a friend whose father is so wealthy he has established a trust fund for his children that will begin doling out money after he dies. It doesn't matter to him that his children are already in their fifties and could use the money now—to send their kids to college, to help support an ill wife. Nor does it matter to him that they are all quite capable of managing any money they would receive after his death. He wants to control how much, when, and how they get the money, even after he is dead.

My friend's situation is not unique. I know three other people with parents so committed to control that they hold on even from the grave. Some folks would argue that since the money is theirs, they have a right to say how and when it is used. They may have a point, but don't confuse this outlook with generosity. This approach is simply purchasing something with your money—you behave like this and I will give you that—or expressing your disapproval—you haven't lived the way I want so I will not let you have a say.

True giving says, "Here, take this and do what you think you should with it. I give you freedom. I let go of whatever I think should happen and allow you to do what you think is right." True generosity follows the pattern of nature—the seed lets go of its identity in order for the tree to sprout; the caterpillar lets go of its old form in order to become a butterfly. For the new to emerge, the old generously lets go of form and identity. It doesn't try to cling to itself but graciously gives way.

By clinging, you never get to experience the joy that comes with true giving. I was reminded of that the other day by a friend in her seventies who gave $5,000 to her kids when an annuity of hers came due. "It's more fun to give it," she said, "than it was to get it." So true. The fun comes in giving the gift and watching the other person delightedly receive it. When we put conditions on our giving, we miss out on that wholehearted receiving. My friend's father may end up "giving" his children millions, but he will never receive their thanks, because his stingy conditions preclude any feelings of gratitude.

If You Give, You Will
Be Provided for

*If you help others you will be helped, perhaps tomorrow,
perhaps in one hundred years, but you will be helped.
Nature must pay off the debt. . . . It is a mathematical
law and all life is mathematics.*

—GURDJIEFF

Long before managed care, my father was a small-town family doctor, the old-fashioned kind who made house calls, birthed babies, and comforted the dying when they were beyond medical help. Everyone in town knew him and assumed we were rich because he was a doctor. My father, who grew up in the slums of Boston, was never rich, because he kept his fees low and gave away a lot of care for free.

This was when all the talk was about the coming of socialized medicine. My father didn't believe in it, he said, because he thought every doctor should volunteer to see a percentage of patients for free. If every doctor did, then everyone would have adequate care (and, as a side benefit, all the reimbursement paperwork would be eliminated). When he retired, I helped him close his office. I was supposed to send out final bills, but I just listened to him tell me why so-and-so could not pay and should not be billed. He knew everyone's story.

When I asked him why he wasn't more concerned about money, he said that, given his background, he felt very rich and didn't need any more than he had, and that it was his privilege to give his medical gift to as many people as possible. Our family may never have been affluent but we certainly had all we needed. When my father died, twenty years after retirement, the church was packed with former patients, nurses, and doctors who came to say thanks and good-bye to a man with a big heart.

My father was a person who had his priorities straight. So many of us think that our security lies in accumulating a big wad of cash, and we make that the focus of our lives. Even if we succeed in our stockpiling, stock markets can crash and banks can fail. Our true safety comes in offering our gifts to the world, and trusting that by doing what we love, we will be provided for in return. We may not have the best car, the biggest house, or the yacht in the harbor. We will have the immense satisfaction that comes from using our gifts to their fullest, something no amount of money can buy. By giving our best self to the world, we will be creating a strong network of loving friends, family, and neighbors who will be there for us, no matter what happens.

Let Go of the Ledger Sheet

You have not lived a perfect day, even though you have earned your money, unless you have done something for someone who will never be able to repay you.

—RUTH SMELTZER

I can't say I have measured up to Ruth Smeltzer's yardstick for a perfect day, because there are many, many days that I have not done something for someone else. Despite her high standard, this quote points to something that is crucial to understand about giving: In a sense, the things we do for one another can never be repaid, so when it comes to living from a giving heart, we have to forget the ledger sheet.

Here's what I mean by ledger sheet. Years ago, my husband and I were friends with another couple. It was more of a social friendship than anything else; my husband worked with her husband. She was very proper, and the rules of society dictated that if you were invited to dinner at their house, you must then invite them to yours. You would not be invited back to their house— even if they wished to see you—until you had fulfilled your obligation to feed them.

That's the ledger sheet—you do this and I will repay you by doing that. Somewhere in the back of our minds, we keep track of our giving and receiving to make sure it comes out even. You give me a present worth $100 and I must give something of equal value. In this system, everything, including ourselves, is a commodity, and we must exchange equally or one of us is going to feel ripped off.

This ledger view implies that there is not enough to go around, so things must be very carefully doled out and tracked. Not only is this exhausting, it completely squashes genuine caring because it fails to take into account the circumstances of one another's lives. What if you don't have a home that can host a dinner party, or enough money to take me out to eat? I would never see you. Because I have more money than you, I have to be careful not to give you anything that you can't repay.

Fundamentally, the ledger sheet just doesn't work. How can your husband, for instance, repay you for helping raise his children as a stepparent? Raising kids is an act of love, pure and simple, that has to be given with no strings attached. Otherwise, the burden of guilt will be so heavy on him that he will have to minimize your contribution to feel okay about himself. You will receive no appreciation and the love between you will shrivel up. With the ledger sheet, our caring is always pinched. We have to be afraid—of being "taken

79

advantage of. The person on the receiving end better figure out how to pay up, or they will feel guilty and have to deflect your giving in order to feel equal again.

There's a way to give without the ledger sheet, a way that says, "I feel loving toward you and I want to express that to the level I feel like. Period. I express my caring and you express yours." In the case of the dinner party problem, if I want to see you, let's eat at my house every time. You'll figure out a way to be generous too—perhaps by bringing a great bottle of wine or flowers, or offering to baby-sit my child.

When we give up the ledger sheet and are truly giving what we want to, there's no danger of feeling ripped off. We want to buy her the wreath because we think it will make her happy and we want her to know we love her—not because we want something in return.

I have been working on giving up the ledger sheet over the past few years, and I've been fairly successful. Holidays are my downfall because they come with an expectation of a gift exchange, so I fall into the trap of giving in order to get. If I give a present to someone and don't get one in return, I notice that I feel bad. If I give a gift spontaneously at another time of the year, I feel great. The commercialized gift-giving that accompanies our holidays only reinforces the ledger sheet idea.

You Never Know What the Effects of Your Actions Will Be

"Let me light the lamp,"
says the star,
"And never debate
if it will help to remove the darkness."

—Rabindranath Tagore

My mother has a niece whom she loves very much. This niece has four sons and a life that doesn't allow for many extras. So when the boys were young, my mother, who lives on Cape Cod, used to invite them down each summer for a vacation. One year she decided to pay for sailing lessons for Mike, one of the sons who expressed interest in learning to sail. She knew her niece couldn't afford it on her own. Mike is now in his twenties, and he makes a living sailing around the world. Inadvertently, my mother helped Mike discover his passion and his profession!

My mother's story reminded me that we can never know what the effects of our actions will be. All we can do is live from our hearts and trust that the goodness we do will ripple out into the world. We can't get too attached to a particular outcome. By paying for the sailing lessons, my mother wasn't trying to turn Mike into a

81

sailor, she just was offering him a chance to sail.

Buddhist teacher Jack Kornfield has a story about the problems with having strings attached to our giving. Kornfield was a young monk in Asia, where beggars abound. He would go back and forth to the temple to meditate, passing the beggars every day. Finally he was about to leave the area and, filled with compassion, he decided to take what money he could afford, have it changed into many bills of small denominations, and, looking each person in the eyes and bowing respectfully, hand over the money. It was to be an offering of respect as well as money, done mindfully to each person.

He walked up to the first beggar and all went according to plan. He looked deeply into his eyes, he bowed, he carefully handed over the money. As soon as the other beggars saw the money, they immediately began to mob him. All sense of ceremony was lost as they scrambled for the cash. He ended up throwing all the money into the air and running like hell!

We give because we want to give. We don't give so it will turn out a certain way, or because we will get thanked. We give because we want to experience the joy that comes from offering whatever it is that is ours to offer. In the words of T. S. Eliot, "For us, there is only the trying. The rest is not our business."

All True Giving Is Loving

*Love has nothing to do with what you are expecting
to get—only what you are expecting to give.*

—KATHERINE HEPBURN

I heard a great story recently about a young man who, fired up with religious teachings on compassion and generosity, decided to make a bunch of peanut butter and jelly sandwiches so he could give them away to homeless people in his neighborhood. He couldn't give away even one sandwich. Nobody wanted what he had to offer. So he thought to himself, "This giving thing is more complicated than I thought. If I really want to be helpful, maybe I should find out what these people want."

The next day, he went out empty-handed. All he did was say hello to a few people and strike up a conversation about the weather. The next day he again spoke to the same people, this time asking a bit about how they were doing. This went on for a while, until he discovered that what they really wanted was something sweet—sandwiches were the main fare at the homeless shelters. He began to make brownies, incredible, wonderful brownies, and offer those along with conversation.

This young man discovered that to truly give, you

must know what is wanted. To know that, you must form a relationship with the other—you have to love them. Love is merely the willingness to know the other person as he or she truly is, and then offering yourself as you truly are. This man was willing to drop all expectations of how he thought homeless people should be—that a hungry person should want a peanut butter sandwich or even that a hungry person should be grateful for anything—to discover who they actually were and then offer what he could of who he was. That's as wonderful an act of love as any other I know of.

In love, we look outside of ourselves at the other and want the best for them. In love, we feel our hearts swell as we seek to bring happiness or peace or comfort to the other. What is true giving except these very things?

In order to truly give, we need to actually see the people we are reaching out to. We need to understand that, just like us, they want to be happy. We need to recognize that, just like us, they are suffering. And from this awareness, our loving compassion is born.

When we remember that giving is loving, we are able to be more accurate in our giving. When we experience giving as loving, we feel the joy that our generous actions can bring.

Think Positive!

*Gladness is akin to goodness. The world needs all the
help you can give by way of cheerful, optimistic,
inspiring thought and personal example.*

—GRENVILLE KLEISER

My business partner, Will, and I lived together
for fourteen years. Whenever we got into a
hard place with one another and I complained about our
relationship to my friend Daphne, she would always ask
me why I stayed with him. The question wasn't meant
as criticism of my choice, but was her way to remind me
of the good things about our relationship. I would
always give the same answer: "Because he is cheerful
every single day." Since I find it easy to sink down into
depression, his upbeat temperament was a true joy to be
around. Eventually, I decided I wanted to cultivate my
own positiveness instead of being dependent on someone else to provide it. While I don't pretend to be as
practiced at it as a lifelong optimist, I'm trying.

My efforts in this direction are the most generous
thing I can do for those around me. Cynicism, alien-
ation, and disaffection abound in our society. It's not
cool to be hopeful, to be cheerful, to be optimistic, or to
care too much.

85

Such cynicism is a cover. We've been hurt somewhere along the line and want to make sure we're not hurt again. Giving up hope and caring, we reason, will protect us from further pain. Sealed off in our bubble of misery, however, we are continually injured by our old hurt. Have you ever met a pessimist who was happy and not just content in his or her misery? Pessimists are too busy protecting themselves from pain to feel anything but pain. Only by risking happiness and hoping, even trusting, in a good outcome do we have any hope of rising out of our personal misery.

This is true with our approach to the external world. Instead of being immobilized by our cynicism, which allows for no movement at all and increases the possibility of bad things happening, we should strive for optimism and hope for the best. Optimism, even learned optimism like mine, creates the possibility of movement and of discovering solutions. Hope and cheerfulness create the energy that opens us to the possible future and the potentially good outcome. Adopting a can-do attitude is the most generous thing we can do right now. The more of us who adopt it, the more the force of positive change will be unleashed in the world. Now that's a gift that's worth giving!

Strive for Balance

It is better to give and receive.

—BERNARD GUNTHER

About a year ago, two authors of mine, a couple, offered to let me use their house in Hawaii. "Thank you," I said politely, "I can't get over there now, but I appreciate the offer." Inside, I was feeling terribly uncomfortable. It was such a generous offer and I didn't know them very well; how could I possibly take them up on it? I wondered if they really meant it.

Several months later, they repeated the offer, with the same results. I deflected their kindness and felt embarrassed and confused. Then I ran into them again and we went through the same process. As I walked away, something changed in me. It was partly because I had just read something about Buddha and Jesus never refusing anyone who asked them something three times. Mostly it was that I was beginning to think about generosity and wanted to examine what was going on more closely.

I realized that they must really mean it—after all, they did offer three times. I understood that they had appreciated what I had done for them as an editor and wanted to demonstrate their gratitude. By constantly refusing, I was not allowing them to express their thanks to me.

I had a part in this exchange, too. Even though it's hard for me to be on the receiving end in general, I felt unworthy to receive such a generous gesture. Taking in the idea that someone wanted to do something so nice for me was painful, and that was standing in my way of getting to have a wonderful experience.

I came to understand that receiving is as important as giving, otherwise no gift would ever find its home. The receiver has an important part in the process. It takes grace to say, "Yes, I would love that," or "That would be wonderful, thank you." It implies that you believe you are worth getting whatever it is that is being offered. I was used to being in the position of "giver." That felt comfortable and safe to me. I could give and feel good about myself in the giving. But feeling good in the receiving was a whole new frontier. I decided to call the couple up and say yes. I went and had a marvelous time in their beautiful retreat. While I must admit it still felt a bit awkward, I remembered that all new behavior feels awkward because we haven't practiced it much.

Are you off-balance as well? Is it easy for you to give but not to receive? Are you comfortable receiving and withhold in your giving? Being generous is a two-sided process, and experiencing both sides is vital to our well-being and growth. Without giving, we become cut off from the human family; without receiving, we are in danger of becoming burned-out, resentful wrecks.

It's Both an Inside and Outside Job

*There is a pervasive form of contemporary violence to
which the idealist ... most easily succumbs: ... activism
and overwork. ... To allow oneself to be carried away by a
multitude of conflicting concerns, to surrender to too many
demands, to commit oneself to too many people, to want to
help everyone in everything, is to succumb to violence.
The frenzy ... kills the root of inner wisdom
which makes work fruitful.*

—THOMAS MERTON

When I was in my twenties, I was, like so many others in the late '60s and early '70s, convinced that I could change the world merely through the force of my desire for it to change. I lived in a large commune dedicated to social and political change, and the twenty of us who lived there spent every waking moment rushing to meetings, holding events, picketing, and marching. We may have screamed for peace and bullied others to be more tolerant and understanding, but we felt good about ourselves. At least we were giving—unlike all those unfeeling, lazy, middle-class slobs all around us.

Inside of myself, however, something felt profoundly wrong. The problem, it seemed to me, was not just with the "system" but with the way we were relating to it. It didn't seem right to be so angry or so violent. We never had time to look at ourselves, even if we had wanted to, though. We were too busy.

Over time, like so many other people, I drifted away from activism. Not because I had lost my ideals, but because I didn't know how to actualize them. I spent time on myself; I helped raise a family. I always felt bad because I wasn't giving to the world in the way I thought I should. How could I make a difference, though? My previous attempt had been so useless.

One day, I heard Vietnamese monk Thich Nhat Hanh speak of the peace activists he had met in the United States. "They want peace, but they aren't peaceful. To have peace, you must be peace." I realized that my fellow activists and I had been busy trying to create peace around us but we were anything but peaceful inside.

With this realization, I really came to see that true giving has two aspects. One is internal, the cultivation of wisdom within yourself so that your gift is both appropriate and skillfully offered. The other is external, the actual proffering of time, money, skills, perspective, or commitment. Like the balance needed between giving and receiving, the inside and outside components of giving need to be in balance as well. If we just "work on ourselves," the wisdom we cultivate goes unused, like a farmer who refuses to harvest his crop. If we spend all our time running around trying to save the world, as Thomas Merton points out, we never develop—or we lose track of—the inner qualities that allow our generosity to be fruitful. Only in stillness can such qualities of character be born, and only in living them out can they ever become actualized.

To grow our giving hearts, we need to engage in a beautiful dance of reaching out and then turning in, action and reflection, movement and stillness. The cultivation of both our inner and outer lives is where true generosity resides.

We Are God's Hands in the World

God's work must truly be our own.

—JOHN F. KENNEDY, IN HIS INAUGURAL ADDRESS

There is a wonderful Sufi teaching story about a spiritual seeker who was praying outside. As he prayed, he noticed a constant stream of beggars, people crippled in body and mind or in spirit and heart, go past him. He looked at this mass of suffering humanity and, lifting his voice to God cried, "Great God, how is it that a loving creator can see such things and yet do nothing about them?"

Then, out of the long silence, came the voice of God, saying, "I did do something. I made you."

That story never fails to inspire me, no matter how many times I read it. The world is full of misery and full of great physical and emotional hardships. Sometimes I think about what humans endure—starvation, war, the death of loved ones, abuse, torture—and am amazed that life goes on at all. All the great spiritual traditions address the fact of human suffering, and each of us has to somehow wrap her mind around it, too.

Life is more than suffering. It also contains joy, laughter, and renewal. Life contains peace, beauty, and contentment. It contains human beings with the consciousness to be aware of suffering and who want to do something about it. We are God's hands, voice, and eyes on Earth. Because we are aware of suffering, we are also capable of compassion and empathy. Through our compassion, we can reach out to offer our arms to a person who needs a hug or their burden carried, if only for a little while. We can offer a kind or encouraging word, or a look that says, "I see what you are going through. Is there anything I can do to help?"

When we act in empathy and compassion, we make God's love incarnate. We become, as the Christian hymn says, like "angels descending, bring from above, echoes of mercy, whispers of love."

God has no hands but ours. How will you use yours?

The Practice of Giving

Don't we all need some concrete form of retraining so that we may learn to be more generous and let go more gracefully? We all—each of us without exception— have so much to give if we only knew it.

—LAMA SURYA DAS

This chapter addresses the practices we can use to expand our experience of giving. We go beyond our feelings of openheartedness to specific behaviors that will bring that feeling alive in the world. The ultimate goal is expressing our feelings of generosity in a variety of ways that bring joy to ourselves and others. The more we do, the more we will experience firsthand the ultimate grace of the giving heart—happiness, contentment, and the enlargement of the soul that comes when we live from, in the words of Sharon Salzberg, "a heart as wide as the world."

Become More Aware of Your Generosity

*There is nothing forced or self-disciplined about
[generosity].... [A generous person] goes out of his way,
not because his parents taught him that's how good [people]
behave, but because he has chosen to be alert to the
circumstances in which he can be supportive.*

—TIBOR R. MACHAN

My friend Dawna Markova is the most generous person I know. Before starting this book, the first thing I did was to talk to her. I asked her about her own generosity—where she thought it came from and what her relationship to it was. Normally a fount of wisdom on every subject, she was, at first, uncharacteristically silent. Finally she said, "I don't know what to say. It's such a value to me, such a part of my training, that it's like asking a fish to describe water." She went on to be her usual brilliant self on the subject, but that initial hesitation stuck with me.

There have been several studies done on kidney donors to determine what makes someone willing to give a part of their own body to another person. In almost every single case, the donor felt it was no big deal. It didn't seem like a sacrifice, or something that had to be mulled over. Someone was in need and they were glad to be able to respond.

In his book *Generosity*, Tibor Machan claims generosity is a virtue we can choose to cultivate or not, but that once we choose to cultivate it, it becomes invisible to us. When we operate from our sense of generosity, we don't have to think about whether we're going to give something. We just do. What differentiates generosity from charity, he claims, is its lack of deliberation. With charity, we have a sense that we should give something to another person or a cause because it is the right thing to do. When we operate from generosity, we don't even think about right or wrong. We just give as a matter of course.

The ways we are generous are invisible to us because they are a natural part of our being. Without hesitating, we'll drive an extra hour out of our way to pick up Grandma, or we'll schedule time to speak to a friend's daughter who is thinking about a career in our field. No matter how busy we are, we'll call a friend who has just suffered a loss.

It's wonderful to have generous impulses, but the problem with the invisibility of your generosity is that you can have all kinds of false perceptions about your ability to give. All of the wonderful things you give as a matter of course may be completely off your radar screen. In my case, I think of myself as someone who is stingy with money. After reading about the kidney donors, though, I remembered that I lent my sister a pretty big sum so she'd have enough for a down payment to buy a house. Despite my money fears, giving to my sister was such an "of course," that my act didn't even register on my internal self-monitor.

Take a few moments to remind yourself of the ways you have been generous in the past and are being so now. Bring all the ways you are giving into the light of your awareness and celebrate them.

Look at Your Gifts

What are the gifts that we've been given?
To deny that we are gifted is, perhaps, to indulge in
false humility, which allows us to shirk responsibility for
the gift. But the gift is a sacred trust. . . . It asks that
we develop it. And it asks that we pass it on.

—DEENA METZGER

I have been an editor for twenty-two years. I'm good at it, and I know I'm good. Recently I was meeting with a well-known writer for the first time. She asked me something—perhaps how I could help her—and part of what I said was, "Well, I'm really good at looking at something and knowing what goes where, and what else might be needed. It's just a gift I have of being able to see the whole and the parts at the same time." She hired me on the spot, not only, she said, because I could help her, but because she sees herself as very insecure, and it was a great gift to her that I was so able matter-of-factly to acknowledge my ability.

Perhaps it is easy for me to acknowledge my talents because in some way I don't feel I "own" them. They have been given to me, and it is my sacred duty to cultivate them and my sacred honor to pass them on. I have been given the ability to analyze, and it is my both my obligation and my delight to offer that to the world.

Before we can offer our gifts, we need to know what they are, which can be difficult for many people. We are taught to be modest, to downplay our strengths, and to focus on our faults. It begins in childhood when everyone around us at school and at home is fixated on what we are doing wrong, instead of what's right about us. As a consequence, we grow up unaware of the very precious gifts that have been given to us to use.

To begin to know who we are and what we are here to offer, we need to look at what we've already given in our lives and what we've received. From there, we can begin to create a more accurate picture of where our gifts are and what our purpose here on Earth might be.

Here's an exercise from Deena Metzger's wonderful book *Writing for Your Life:* Make two lists, one of gifts you've given and one of gifts you've received. After you are done, look at both of these lists as if you just found them on the street corner and you know nothing else about the person who wrote them. Then, writes Metzger, "develop a portrait of the person who emerges from this series of exchanges by examining the nature of the lists, the kinds and qualities of the gifts given and received, and their relationship to one another. . . . Who is this person?"

Set Your Intention

A hundred times every day I remind myself that
my inner and outer life depends on the labors of other men,
living and dead, and that I must exert myself in order to give
in the measure as I have received and am still receiving.

—ALBERT EINSTEIN

It's so easy to get busy in our own lives, to shut down our awareness and see only what needs to be done in front of us instead of anyone or anything else. I often find myself bustling around, so focused on getting my list done that I don't even take time to say hello to people in the office. Sometimes I find myself walking out the door when someone is still speaking to me! If they did need something of me, how would I know? I'm moving too fast for it to even register.

Because my life is so full and so speeded up, I find it helpful to take a moment when I wake up and set my intention to be helpful to others that day. The phrase I say is very simple—"May I be of use"—but it has profound effects. It focuses me on what is most important and reminds me that meeting the deadline, for example, is important, but not as important as being caring to those I meet throughout the day. Setting this intention makes it more likely that when I do get speedy and unconscious of those around me, I will take a deep breath and look around at those with whom I am sharing this life.

This is what Einstein means. We will get busy and self-involved, and forget to notice anything but ourselves. Even though we will forget every single day, if we set our intention we create a base to go back to. We can begin to notice when we are forgetting and return to our resolution to live by our giving heart.

Give it a try. Tomorrow, when you wake up, ask to be of use as you go through your day. It needs to be in your own words, from your heart. Here are some examples: "May I make a difference in the world today." "May I be of service to one person." "May I notice myself and others." "May I give the gift that only I can give." Notice how that reverberates throughout the day.

If you prefer, you can say this beautiful verse by the Dalai Lama:

103

> May I become at all times/both now and forever/
> A protector for those without protection/A guide
> for those who have lost their way/A ship for those
> with oceans to cross/A sanctuary for those in
> danger/A lamp for those without light/A place of
> refuge for those who lack shelter/And a servant to
> all in need.

Begin Somewhere

*What one does is what counts and not
what one had the intention of doing.*

—PABLO PICASSO

I don't know about you, but I am full of good intentions. I intend to do yoga, meditate every morning, and create Ana's adoption scrapbook. Tomorrow. Somehow tomorrow never comes, or more accurately, tomorrow comes, but I am stuck in the same ruts and routines as today, so my good intentions go nowhere. Like any new behavior, we have to stop talking about it and begin to do it. Somewhere, somehow—but where and how?

This past year, I had the privilege of working with Jackie Waldman, the author of *The Courage to Give: Inspiring Stories of People Who Triumphed Over Tragedy to Make a Difference in the World.* It's a series of profiles of people who have suffered great physical or emotional difficulties and healed themselves by reaching out to help others. It's partly Jackie's story too—she has multiple sclerosis, and she has found that the more she gives to others, the better she feels physically and emotionally. Her discovery amazed her, and in her desire to see whether this happened to other people as well, she found many people for whom this was true. Her book, and its follow-up companion *Teens with the Courage to Give*, provide substance to Edwin Markham's words that "all that we send into the lives of others comes back into our own."

As a result of her books, Jackie has become a national spokesperson for the transformative power of volunteerism. I spoke to her recently about giving, and she said that virtually everyone she meets wants to be helpful to others but many of us don't know where to start. "I've learned in these situations," she said, "to ask people three questions. That's all it takes: (1) What do you love to do? (2) To whom do you feel drawn to lend a hand? (3) Is there something that speaks to your heart?" Today, ask yourself these questions and listen deeply to the answers. Then, armed with the information from your heart, you can try logging onto *volunteermatch.org*, plug in your responses, and find all kinds of choices right in your own backyard.

Share What You Love

Don't worry about what the world wants from you,
worry about what makes you come more alive. Because what
the world really needs are people who are more alive.

—LAWRENCE LA SHAN

My friend Andy is a wonderful bodyworker. Among other things, he does Touch For Health, which is a system for finding out what substances, like vitamins and minerals, your body needs. In the ten years I have known him, he's offered his knowledge to me and many other people, as well as teach the system to several people. I've never seen him charge one penny. Helping people is something that makes him come alive, and sharing it makes him feel good. My husband Don has an intuitive gift for picking stocks and has made a lot of money at it. Recently he has begun to e-mail stock suggestions to friends, not because he wants a commission, but because it feels good to be using his talent and he wants to share it with others.

We all have things we love to do that make us come alive. I love to edit. Although I do it to make a living, I also give it away for "free" to friends who want me to look at a proposal they're writing, a novel they're penning, or a letter they're sending. Editing makes me feel more alive, and I am grateful for the chance to feel that exhilaration whenever the opportunity presents itself. It's similar to a racehorse wanting to run as fast as it can or a great skier wanting to swoop down the mountain. It just feels good to use your abilities to the utmost. Sharing that good feeling with someone else by imparting your knowledge is just icing on the cake.

Think about what you love to do. List a few items to yourself: I love to make quilts; I enjoy fixing cars; I love archeology. Imagine that the things you love are jewels that you keep locked up tight in a jewelry box instead of taking them out and wearing them. By keeping them locked up, you miss out on the enjoyment of wearing them and using them, and other people miss out on seeing them and maybe trying them on.

Try wearing that diamond or displaying that emerald. Think of one thing you could do for others by doing what you love. Get a group together to make crib quilts for hospitalized crack babies. Teach some inner city kid to fix a car. Take a group out on an archeological trip around your town. Start with what you love and the intention to share it, and the rest will be easy.

Cultivate Compassion

The worse people act, the greater is their need for healing.

—A COURSE IN MIRACLES

I was walking in the crosswalk on a busy street in San Francisco this past Christmas, and a dapper older gentleman, dressed to the nines with a hat and a cane, was walking down the street toward me. I was just about to reach the curb when a taxi turning right on the red light almost plowed into me. I stopped to make sure it wouldn't hit me, and then, when I knew that the taxi driver had seen me, I continued walking. As I did, the old man suddenly blurted out, "Wake up you ******* *****." I walked a couple more steps and then turned around, trying to verify that he had been addressing his obscenities to me. Seeing me turn, he said, "Yes, I mean you, you ******* *****."

I was shocked. I had done nothing to provoke him; he was quite far from me so I hadn't cut him off or slowed him down. As the shock wore off, I remembered the quote from *A Course in Miracles* and felt great compassion. What must have happened to this man in his life that he felt the need to say such a thing to me?

This realization has come in handy many other times—when someone is verbally attacking me, or when I learn about back-stabbing comments someone has made. If I can see their need for healing instead of shutting down, running, or attacking, I can engage my compassion. I can offer silent wishes that they be healed once I recognize that they must be in some kind of pain to behave in such a hurting way. Even when I find myself behaving in a less than stellar way, I acknowledge my need for healing and apologize.

Increasing my compassion allows me to stay connected to my heart and lets me release the full power of my generosity. Disconnecting from our compassion means that there is no possibility we can give to others. Sealed off from our loving nature, we can't see whatever need might be presenting itself.

Remaining compassionate is not easy, particularly when we are under attack. In her column in the *Shambhala Sun*, therapist Karen Kissel Wegela offers this strategy, called the Difficult Person exercise. Sit quietly alone for a few minutes. Then, imagine that the Difficult Person (DP) is sitting across from you at eye level. For a few minutes, bring this person into as much vivid detail as you can. Now imagine that you are the DP. Notice what is it like to be in his or her body. How old are you? Are you in pain? What emotions are you feeling?

In the role of the DP, look across at you. What do you want from this person who is having such a hard time with you? Imagine that you, the DP, actually got what you needed from this other person. What would it feel like to have received it?

Become yourself again and look at the DP. How does it feel to have given him or her what was needed? Is it possible for you to really do this? As Wegela notes, people who do this exercise often discover "that what the DP wanted was something much simpler than what we had thought. Often it is easy for us to imagine giving it to them, and we find we become more tender." At the very least, this exercise makes it easier for us to understand their pain, and why they might be treating us poorly. That discovery is enough to open our hearts.

Surprise Someone

*Giving brings happiness at every stage of
its expression. We experience joy in forming the intention
to be generous; we experience joy in the actual act of giving
something; and we experience joy in remembering
the fact that we have given.*

—BUDDHA

lizabeth had planned a surprise weekend ski trip for her husband's fortieth birthday. She had called his boss and gotten him Friday off, she'd arranged for someone to watch the kids, and she'd booked the hotel. The week before the trip, she and her husband went over the family finances and discovered they were in a big hole. With these new financial difficulties, Elizabeth felt that she couldn't afford the cost of the trip, but it was the perfect gift. What was she going to do? After talking to her friend Sue, she decided to turn the weekend into a one-night stay at a nearby hotel that was having a special on their rates. Even this trip would cost the exact amount of that week's bonus. It wasn't perfect, but she would make do. That Thursday, she told her husband she was taking him on an adventure the next day.

When they arrived at the hotel to check in, she was surprised to find a note saying that they had been upgraded to a suite with a fireplace and a hot tub. After they had settled in, a cart with champagne and strawberries was delivered to their suite. The next day, each had a massage, which had already been paid for. Elizabeth and her husband later found out that Sue had decided to surprise them both. When they called to thank her, Sue said that she'd had a fabulous year in her business and wanted to spread it around.

Surprising someone is a particularly delightful kind of giving, one that shows the true happiness of giving. Being new to the practice of surprises myself, I've really noticed how much fun they are for the giver. I still get a smile on my face when I remember tucking a $10 bill in the cart of a homeless person when he was poking in a trash can, or the time I hid $100 in my stepdaughter's backpack as she set off for a summer in Europe.

This kind of giving is easy to practice. All it takes is some ingenuity.

Do What's Needed

*Too many people are ready to carry the stool
when the piano needs moving.*

—ANONYMOUS

I love this quote so much that I included it here, even though I also used it in *More Random Acts of Kindness*™. It reminds me that even though we may want to pick and choose what to give, going with what's convenient or what's fun, sometimes we just need to do what's needed. Sometimes we just have to get in there and heft that piano because our friend is moving and needs our help. Perhaps the postage meter broke but the letters need to go out anyway. So we lick 300 stamps, even though we would rather be answering our e-mail.

I have noticed that there are folks who pitch in and joyfully do what is needed (the givers), people who begrudgingly do it (the resenters), and those that seem always to disappear whenever something extra needs to be done (the withholders). "Not in my job description," they say, which is true.

These resenters and withholders miss out on the joy of pitching in together with others to work on something. They miss the sense of satisfaction when the task is completed. They also miss the happiness that comes

113

from actually doing something you know is needed right now, and which will be helpful, even if only in a small way. So much of what most of us do day to day is invisible, and I always relish the times when someone comes along and says, "I need help on this." It makes my efforts more concrete and gives me something specific that I can point to as I think, "I helped make this happen."

To experience this sense of satisfaction, try this experiment. The next time someone at the office or home is looking for help, offer to pitch in. Then pay close attention to how it makes you feel.

Look at Your Generosity Teachers

Make yourself necessary to someone.

—Ralph Waldo Emerson

While writing *Attitudes of Gratitude*, I learned something about myself that I never realized before. I constantly seek out people who have characteristics I wanted to cultivate. I meet someone and notice her strengths, and if I want to learn this strength, I create a lasting connection with this person. Thirty years ago in high school, I latched onto a young teacher because she seemed to have the love of books and the cultured appreciation of the world I desired, and we've been friends ever since. Over the years, I've picked friends who were incredibly loving so I could learn about love, friends who were exceptionally happy and grateful so I could learn about happiness and gratitude, and friends who were great mothers so I could learn about mothering.

The first generosity teacher I had was my father. A big guy of six-foot-two, he inevitably gave me the biggest steak or the extra pork chop instead of keeping it for himself because I was a meat lover. I noticed him doing it week in and week out, without ever saying anything about it. I realized that this is how you give without out drawing attention to yourself.

My next teacher in giving was Will Glennon. I was twenty-five when we met; he was thirty. He was at the helm of the weekly newspaper that we were both working on. Anyone who has ever worked on a newspaper knows how fast-paced it is—every week, a handful of people must make a sixty-page paper come out on time. I soon noticed how generous Will was whenever someone interrupted him with a question, which was every two minutes or so. He never said, "Go away. I'm busy writing three stories." Instead, he always stopped, smiled, and said, "What can I do for you?" I vowed then and there to cultivate that same kind of graceful generosity when it came to offering help.

Will became my teacher by being generous with money while we were living together. We were well off during some of those years, and he never said no when asked to donate to a cause. He had the money and he gave it away unthinkingly. Watching him, I realized that this too was something to be learned.

I've learned many things about having a giving heart from the people in my life. As Gary Zukav said, "As you come to seek and see the virtues and strengths and nobilities of others, you begin to seek and see them in yourself also." I've experienced generosity as an abundance of love from Dawna; as the willingness to stick with something difficult with someone no matter how long it takes from Daphne; as the capacity to be truly more concerned with others than yourself from Jackie. As a result of their examples, I have given more in various dimensions than I probably would have previously. I've opened my home to friends in need; I've given trips to friends who could not afford them; I've tried to give my all to the people I work with.

Who has taught you what you know about living from a giving heart? What specific lessons about generosity did you learn? How do you enact them now? What do you still want to learn? Is there someone in your life that you could learn from? Don't be afraid to ask this person for help. Having your positive qualities acknowledged is a great gift within itself.

117

Include Yourself

*We should ask the question whether we are capable
of loving ourselves as well as others. Are we treating our
body kindly—by the way we eat, by the way we drink, by
the way we work? Are we treating ourselves with
enough joy and tenderness and peace?*

—THICH NHAT HANH

My friend Ginger and I both love to read. We read novels voraciously and then furiously trade them back and forth across three states. Recently she went to the bookstore, she said, and bought me five novels. On the way to mail them, she realized that she was giving me what she really wanted for herself. She had run out of books to read, but somehow it was easier for her to buy them for me than for herself. In the end, she decided that she had bought the books for herself and that she would send them to me when she was finished.

Somehow we think that generosity and self-sacrifice go hand in hand. It's probably a result of ledger-sheet thinking again—if I give something to you, then I must lose something for myself. That model—that resources are finite and that if I do something nice for you I must go without—is very deeply entrenched in our thinking. Practicing self-generosity as we deepen our giving helps get us out of the either/or view most of us are stuck in.

Self-generosity is simply doing unto yourself what you would do for others. Many of us give what we most want to receive, and once we recognize that truth we can easily figure out what we need to give ourselves. Do you spend hours on the phone listening to other people's problems? Perhaps you need to spend some time listening to yourself. Do you love to give flowers to your sweetheart? Perhaps you need to give a bouquet to yourself, for no reason except that it will bring you pleasure.

Self-generosity doesn't have to be confined to the things we do for others; that's just a good place to begin. On a wider scale, self-generosity is the attitude that says, "I am as deserving of my own care and attention as anyone else, and I am going to act toward myself with loving kindness on a regular basis." The forms it takes will be as unique as each of us.

Try this experiment: The next time you find yourself doing something generous to someone else, also do something nice for yourself. It could be the same thing—you listened to your best friend complain about her marriage for forty-five minutes, so now you will listen to yourself with equal exquisite attention by writing in your journal for forty-five minutes. It could be something different—you wrote a college letter of recommendation for a friend's daughter, so you take yourself out to a beautiful lunch. Give yourself something wonderful the next time you do something wonderful for someone else.

Notice the effect it has on you. Is it more likely that you will be generous to yourself and others in the future?

Just Say Yes

Compassion is not quantitative. Certainly it is true
that behind every human being who cries out for help there may
be a million or more equally entitled to attention. . . . How to
determine which of one million sounds surrounding you is more
deserving than the rest? Do not concern yourself in such
speculations. You will never know; you will never need to
know. Reach out and take hold of the one
who happens to be nearest.

—NORMAN COUSINS

I have a very hard time figuring out how to relate to homeless people. Because I'm mad that homelessness exists, I give to organizations that attempt to solve the problem at the fundamental level. I know whatever I put into homeless people's hand or cup will not solve the problem of their homelessness, but there they are— lying on the pavement, sitting on curbs, or standing at freeway on ramps holding signs. I have tried all kinds of things: not giving to anyone no matter what, which seems so cold; giving to everyone no matter what, which isn't possible when you live near a city like San Francisco that has so many homeless people; giving them vouchers for food instead of cash so the money goes to feeding their bellies and not their addiction; or

121

buying food and giving that. No matter what I do, it doesn't feel right.

My actions don't feel right because homelessness shouldn't exist in such an affluent society. Homelessness makes me uncomfortable, as it should, but my discomfort doesn't absolve me from not taking action. This sets up an awkward situation, but I found my personal solution. After remembering that someone wise said we should respond, "Yes," when asked to help, I decided to follow that advice. If someone on the street asks me for money, I give it. If not, I don't. This strategy may leave out many worthy but silent folk, but as Norman Cousins stated, just reach out and take hold of one.

Now I always say "Yes" whenever I'm asked to help out. I said "Yes" when someone asked me to host twin fourteen-year-old Vietnamese-French exchange students for a month, and said "Yes" when I was asked to donate my time to a new spiritual magazine. Instead of volunteering, I wait until asked and then say "Yes." There is more need than any of us can respond to, and this is just my way of deciding where to put my time and attention. I believe that if I am specifically asked, then it is my task to do. This way, I ensure that I respond to the needs all around me, but I don't know what I would do if I were asked to volunteer all the time.

We all need to discover a way to say "Yes." A friend of mine says he figures out what to do by following his generous impulses without second-guessing himself. "If I think about it, I do it, no questions asked," he remarked. In his book *Bring the Full Tithe*, Reverend William D. Watley suggests what he calls "Spirit-led giving." "Spirit-led giving occurs when we earnestly seek God's direction as to what we should give and then ask God's help in making a way for us to give it."

What is your way? If you're not sure, try my strategy for a while. The next few times you are specifically asked to do something for someone, say "Yes." Then notice whether this criterion for giving suits you or not.

Learn Your No Signals

Almost anything is easier to get into than out of.

—AGNES ALLEN

*f*or years I constantly found myself in the same trap. I wanted to see myself as a loving, giving person. My spouse or kids would ask something of me that I believed a kind, generous person would acquiesce to, so I would say "Yes," truly believing that was how I felt. Halfway through the experience, I would find myself flying into a rage of resentment, and then I'd feel guilty for being angry. I began to study the pattern and realized that whenever this happened, I really had wanted to say "No" but didn't realize that until my anger signaled my true answer. The trick was to begin to learn my no before I got mad.

Proclaiming that we should say "No" when we feel like it in order to feel the flow of generosity more strongly in our lives is very different from recognizing when we want to say "No." So many of us have been so well trained in compliance that we don't even know until later that our true desire was a big no.

The answer to our true generosity lies in our bodies. Here's a great practice adapted from Andy Bryner's and Dawna Markova's *An Unused Intelligence.* Start by taking five minutes to notice what you are aware of in the present moment. Note the data that your senses experience and speak or write that down. For example, "I feel my feet resting on the floor; I feel my chest rising and falling with my breath; I see a beam of light on the floor; I hear the sound of laughter." Just take down the facts—unembellished sensory data, no comparisons, no analysis, and no stories. Do not, for example, embellish the sound with something like "I hear the sarcastic laughter of some nasty creep."

Now think of an activity you don't like, perhaps something you do begrudgingly or with resentment. Do that activity for a little while, again noticing the sensory data. How does it make you feel? What sensations might be your body's signals of No? Do you get a tightness in the stomach? A pain in the head? A sense of constriction around your heart? A feeling of curling up in general? When I do this activity, I notice a sinking feeling in the pit of my stomach, as well as a tube of pressure that runs from my stomach to my throat.

Write down what you learned about your body's signals of No. The next time you are doing something you know you don't want to do, notice your body's sensations again. Are they the same or different? Resist telling yourself any story about it or saying, "I shouldn't

Keep the Gift in Motion

Follow through on all your generous impulses.

—Epictetus

Have you ever thought about where the derogatory term "Indian giver" came from? According to Lewis Hyde's book *The Gift*, it was coined in the mid-1700s when the Puritans were first encountering the Indians in Massachusetts.

"Imagine a scene," writes Hyde. "An Englishman comes into an Indian lodge and his hosts, wishing to make their guest feel welcome, ask him to share a pipe of tobacco. Carved from a soft red stone, the pipe itself is a peace offering that has traditionally circulated among the local tribes, staying in each lodge for a time but always given away sooner or later. And so the Indians, as is only polite among their people, give the pipe to their guest when he leaves. The Englishman is tickled pink. What a nice thing to send back to the British Museum! A time passes and the leaders of a neighboring tribe come to visit the colonist's home. To his surprise he finds his guests have some expectation in regard to his pipe"— they want him to give it to them! "In consternation the Englishman invents a phrase to describe these people with such a limited sense of private property."

Hyde goes onto say that the person with the limited sense was actually the white man, for the Indians "understood the cardinal property of a gift: whatever we have been given is supposed to be given away again, not kept.... As it is passed along, the gift may be given back to the original donor, but this is not essential. In fact, it is better if the gift is not returned but is given instead to some new, third party. The only essential is this: the gift must always move." A gift, says Hyde, is about establishing relationships, and the more it moves, the more connections are made. If a gift stops being given away, it is no longer a gift. (This is such a belief among precapitalist cultures that in folktales around the world, a person who tries to keep a gift tends to die.)

Because we live in a capitalist culture where the accumulation of objects is seen to confer status and power, we've lost sight of this notion of gift. Everything we have or "own," however, is a gift from God, the Universe, or the "Great Spirit." Regardless of which source we believe is the giver, the fact that we are alive with the resources we have is an amazing gift. By recognizing this truth, we can begin to see our giving as the Indians did, as a keeping in motion the gift we've received from the benevolence of life.

Here's a simple place to begin. Designate a day as

"giving away" day. Pack up all the clothes you no longer wear. Clean your cupboards of all the pots, pans, utensils, and dishes that you don't use. Do the same for the closets where you store the debris from your life—the kids' old toys, or the lamp you swore you needed but could never find a place for. Pack it all in bags and take it to your favorite charity. (I like to donate things to the battered women's shelter in my town rather than to a thrift store because the women receive the things for free.)

As you go through the process, notice your train of thought. What objects are you willing to let go of? Which ones must you keep? What thoughts go through your mind as you sort? Do you hold onto something, believing that you will need them later even though you haven't used it yet in ten years? Do you think it's too good to give away even though you don't really want it? Do your possessions make you feel safe?

I am a great believer in learning about yourself by trying various behaviors and noticing the effects they have on you. It's crucially important that when you do any of these practices, including this one, you don't use what you discover to harass and judge yourself: See this as an occasion to learn something that can help you let gifts flow more freely in your life.

Practice Agape

An overflowing love which seeks nothing in return,
agape is the love of God operating in the human heart.
At this level, we love men not because we like them, nor because
their ways appeal to us, nor even because they possess some type
of divine spark; we love every man because God loves him.
At this level, we love the person who does an evil deed,
although we hate the deed that he does.

—MARTIN LUTHER KING, JR.

Think of someone you don't particularly like, but whom you see every day. Don't choose someone who has done something truly awful to you; just choose someone who annoys you by doing something that drives you crazy. You can't stand her and just wish she would drop off the face of your Earth.

You have every right to not like this person. As Martin Luther King, Jr., points out in *From Strength to Love*, Jesus didn't direct us to "like" our enemies because liking everyone is too hard. Jesus told us to "love" our enemies instead, and feel a flow of *agape*, which Dr. King defines as the "understanding and creative, redemptive goodwill for all men," toward every human being we come across. That's true generosity of spirit.

For whatever reason, this person is in your world

right now. You can make it as pleasant an experience for yourself and for her, or not. Why not spread as much happiness as you can?

In addition, the fact that she is upsetting you is a clue that you need to learn something through her behavior. Perhaps you envy her certitude and wish you had some of your own, you need to stand up for yourself more, or you realize that you're longing to say how you feel. Whatever the lesson is, you can't discover it if your heart is closed to her. As long as you think her actions are wrong or bad, you'll stay miserable because you will never experience the joy of learning what you can from her.

Here's an activity to try. For one day, focus on something you can appreciate about him or her. You don't have to suddenly love them or want to spend time with them. Just notice some trait they have that you can admire, respect, or enjoy. Everyone has something to appreciate. Are they good with handling annoying customers? Do they always remember to bring in bagels for the team? Do they constantly suggest great creative ideas? Look for this trait; do you feel your heart opening toward them just a crack?

131

Allow Yourself to Be Appreciated

Giving and receiving should be practiced alternately.

—GESHE CHEHAWA

I know a man who works really hard at being generous and helpful. If you have a need, he goes out of his way to try and fill it. He is greatly appreciated by the people in his life but, ironically enough, he feels completely isolated and unappreciated. At times, he can even fall into martyrdom—feeling he gives so much but gets nothing in return.

I think I know why he's stuck in this trap—it is very hard for him to receive any kind of appreciation. He's a master at deflection. When someone says, "Thank you," he responds, "It was nothing." If someone gives him a compliment like, "You're really great at fixing the computers," he acts as if nothing has been said. He literally can't take compliments or thanks in any form, so he is starving for it now. He thinks he isn't being appreciated, but he just can't receive what's right in front of him.

While the rest of us may not be suffering as much as he is, most of us are uncomfortable with appreciation. How many of us respond, "It was no big deal," when someone thanks us for something we did? Or say, "This old thing?" when we are complimented on how great we look in the red shirt we're wearing that day. We think it's polite to minimize our efforts or gifts so that the other person won't feel envious or obliged to us. The person on the other side of the exchange, however, feels differently because he or she is trying to offer something you refuse to receive.

Such "politeness" has insidious effects. Giving and receiving are like an electrical current—two sides of a miraculous exchange of energy—and both need to occur for the circuit to be complete. Otherwise, like in my friend's case, the connection is never made and we remain isolated regardless of which end we're on. Either way, it feels lonely.

If you feel like you are always giving without getting anything in return, try this. Buy a blank book and, for a month, write down every compliment or thanks someone offers you for something that you've done. At the end of the month, go back and read all the appreciation you've received. When my friend tried this, he was amazed to discover how much he tended to ignore the appreciation he was being offered.

133

Give Meaningful Holiday Gifts

The only gift is a portion of thyself.... The poet
brings his poem; the shepherd his lamb ... the girl, a
handkerchief of her own sewing.

—RALPH WALDO EMERSON

Because of my focus on giving, I've spent a lot of time thinking about holidays and the gift-giving that surrounds them, particularly Christmas. For years, I vowed to make my family's Christmas more meaningful. I've tried limiting the number of gifts, I've tried banning presents altogether, and I've even tried leaving town. Despite some inroads, every year I ended up surrounded by a pile of wrapping paper and too many things I do not need or want.

For many of us, holidays that should be filled with opportunities for true happiness—a sense of together-ness, a chance to give, and a chance to be grateful—are turned into occasions for fights, disappointment, over-spending, and fatigue.

Last year, as part of my quest for a more authentic Christmas giving experience, my loved ones and I decided to give one another only presents of time, energy, or creativity. I taught Angie how to cook risotto; Dave took Don skiing for the first time; Andy did a bodywork session with Ana; and Don helped Andy build a closet in the cabin. It was wonderful. We each gave from our knowledge and talents, and we each received knowledge, skills, and experiences in return. To me, it epitomized the best kind of generosity—giving of the self.

Another kind of meaningful holiday giving is making donations to charities in the name of the person you'd normally buy something for. Most of us have so much stuff that we'd prefer not to get yet another blue shirt. By making a donation instead of adding to your aunt's overflowing perfume collection, you give her a part in doing some good for the world.

This book is donating to a charity called My Shopping List for the World (800-842-2243), which offers a wide variety of "good deeds" you can fund—from neighborhood gardens in U.S. inner cities to solar cookers for Kenyan refugees. (See the back of this book for complete information.) The Seva Foundation (510-845-7382) helps restore sight to people in India, Nepal, and Tibet, and also helps indigenous people in Guatemala and Mexico preserve their culture and create sustainable communities; this foundation has a number of very specific gifts that can be given in the someone else's name. World Vision U.S. (800-423-4200), is yet another option; chose from things like giving a goat to a household in Rwanda or literacy training for a child in Bangladesh. AOL Foundation's Helping.org (*www.helping.org*) is a nonprofit organization that will give your gift to any IRS-registered nonprofit without taking any commission.

I'm not asking you to quit doing what you enjoy about holiday gift-giving. I'm suggesting that you take some time to think about what is important to you during the holidays, and to consciously choose to give in a way that truly comes from your heart. Before you get caught up in the next annual frenzy of buying and giving, take stock of your recent experiences. What has had meaning for you? What hasn't? Do you give gifts to social and business acquaintances because it seems necessary? What could you do that reflects your true feelings of appreciation?

Experiment this year by giving one thing that truly comes from yourself. Give people handmade cards or send a letter instead of presents to the relatives you never see. Do whatever you think is necessary to create a more meaningful experience for everyone.

Offer from Overflow

*Thousands of candles can be lighted from a single candle,
and the life of the candle will not be shortened. Happiness
never decreases by being shared.*

—BUDDHA

My friend Fred is a part of an Internet start-up, and he loves the excitement, the creativity, and the "make it up as you go along" feeling. He routinely works twelve to fourteen hour days, and has a wife and two small kids at home. Despite such demands on his schedule, he manages to coach his son's soccer team and often helps friends with their computer problems. He does this all with a joyful spirit. I asked him how he could feel so happy and giving with such a workload. He responded, "My job doesn't leave me much time, but ironically I've discovered that if I take twenty minutes in the morning when I first wake up to be completely quiet and alone, I am then more available to my wife, kids, friends, and coworkers."

How can we give unwaveringly, like a candle, without becoming exhausted, depleted, resentful, or withholding? We can give to ourselves what we give to others; we can actively be on the receiving end; we can realize we can't do everything; and we can say "No" when we mean it. Perhaps the best thing we can do to is to give from overflow, the love we feel flowing from our hearts. To sustain that kind of giving, we need to continually fill ourselves up so that we are full enough to give.

There are two ways to replenish the love we feel flowing from our hearts. First, we need plenty of opportunities in our lives to replenish ourselves. What gives you joy or nourishes you? I find sitting in a hot tub listening to the birds chatter overhead or walking with a friend around the reservoir by my house and looking at the hills change with the seasons replenishes me. How about you? What's on your list?

Once you have your list, think about how often you do these things. Aside from sitting in the hot tub, I haven't done any of them in months, which explains why I've been feeling exhausted and am not inclined to reach out to anyone else. Make a commitment to yourself to add one thing from your list into your daily routine.

A second strategy is developing a practice of renewing ourselves through some of the spiritual energy that is always available. Meditation or prayer is a way many of us get the spiritual renewal we need so we can give from overflow.

Here's a visualization that I like to use, adapted from Sue Patton Thoele's *The Woman's Book of Courage*. Sit quietly and close your eyes. For a few moments, just notice your breathing. When you feel ready, imagine yourself as a vase. Now imagine white light pouring into your vase, filling you up completely. Imagine the energy from the light soaking into every pore, filling every space, and really take in the experience of fullness. When you are ready, open your eyes and notice how you feel. Today, as you go about your work, notice if having been filled has any effect on you.

Let It Be Easy

Anyone who has got any pleasure at all should try to put something back. Life is like a superlative meal and the world is like the maître d'hôtel. What I am doing is the equivalent of leaving a reasonable tip.

—British animal conservationist Gerald Durrell

If I think of giving as tipping, it seems so effortless that I'm much more inclined to do it.

I've had trouble believing that it was okay if something was easy. From early childhood, I thought the proper approach to life was to take it very seriously and work extremely hard. I had contempt for those who didn't try hard—at school, at church—and was convinced that only good deeds that were extraordinarily difficult were worth anything.

Fortunately, I grew out of that attitude, mostly during my twenties, when a friend said to me, "Just because it's easy doesn't mean you shouldn't do it." Like a Zen *koan*, that remark knocked some sense into me, and ever since I've been practicing doing what pleases me and letting it be easy.

A few months ago I got quite excited when someone e-mailed me the address of a Web site called The Hunger Site (*www.thehungersite.com*), which is helping to eliminate hunger around the world. All you have to do is log on and push a button, you don't have to spend a dime or even get up from your desk. This is how the site works—advertisers sponsor at least a week at a time, agreeing to donate the money to purchase half a cup of a staple food in the United Nations World Food Program for each person who logs on and pushes a button. More visitors means more donations, which means more advertisers, and a greater quantity of food. You can only log on once a day, but you can do it every single day. When I logged on today, my donation was up to two cups, and currently the site is sending 1 million cups of food a day to any of the eighty nations the World Food Program serves. The site was started by an individual who wanted to do something about hunger, serving as more proof that an individual can make a huge difference.

What could you do that would be easy for you? The Hunger Site is a good start, but take a few minutes to think about other options as well. Here's an easy way to do this. As you go about your day, at three separate points ask yourself: What would be easy for me to give? Let yourself think over what the answer is, but remember, it doesn't have to be hard.

Bestow the Gift of full Attention

We must not only give what we have;
we must give what we are.

—DESIRE-JOSEPH MERCIER

I have a friend Tom who recently spent a month living in a religious community with about fifty people who live, meditate, and do household work together. "I don't know exactly why," he said to me recently, "but one of the most amazing things about the experience was how exquisitely people would pay attention when you spoke to them. I would come into the kitchen, say, and strike up a conversation with a person sitting there. Soon I would be pouring out my heart about my pain over the break-up of my marriage, and feel so received. And it went both ways—I quickly learned about their struggles and joys as well. I had never experienced anything so intimate in my life."

Tom was experiencing the gift of true presence. Perhaps because the people there spent a great deal of time in silence and in meditation, they were able to bring their full selves and their complete attention to their interactions with one another.

What an incredible gift! How often are any of us really, completely present for someone else? Or for ourselves? I often find myself listening to someone with one part of my mind and thinking about how I will respond, or, as I get older, trying to remember everything I want to say in response. I listen to someone at the office while I sort papers on my desk, I listen to my husband while I get dressed, or I play with Ana while I try to pick up her room at the same time. I seldom drop what I am doing and give my full attention to another human being.

When it comes to paying attention to myself, I can't remember the last time I was completely present for what's really going on inside of me. It tends to leak out in dribbles and drabs as I race through my day, and I catch myself stopping at odd moments to think, "I think I'm upset, what am I upset about?" I don't even know if I am happy or sad, or even delighted or confused.

The generosity of presence is every bit as valuable as money or advice, because the desire to be truly received is at the heart of every human being. Years ago, studies into the value of psychotherapy found that it wasn't any more effective than talking to a caring friend. Merely being listened to was healing.

Try this practice. Sometime soon, really be there for a person who is interacting with you. Stop whatever else you are doing. Sit down with them, or go for a walk. Forget the clock. Really listen, deeply and generously. Resist the impulse to share a story about yourself or to tell the other person what to do. You are there to receive what is being said. When you find your mind wandering, bring it back gently to what he or she is saying. You can even practice on yourself. Ask yourself this very simple question: What is going on for me right now? Write down or tape the answers. Treat yourself as you would the other, just receiving what is being revealed without stories or judgments.

Give Others the Benefit of the Doubt

*We can train ourselves to become more
yielding, balanced, and flexible, giving up
our rigid stances and fixed ideas.*

—LAMA SURYA DAS

D on and I were in one of those arguments that long-time couples tend to have. The ones where whatever you're angry about is fueled by the fact that you've been in exactly this place saying exactly the same things hundreds of times before. I knew that I was right, and I would bet anything that Don was sure he was. I was making one of my impassioned but logical speeches as I tried to get him to come over to my side, but it was going absolutely nowhere. Suddenly he looked at me and said, "You know, I never thought of it that way before. I think you may have a point." That moment changed everything. I felt like he had really heard me, and I could then see his point of view. Soon we were cuddling on the couch, both feeling closer to one another and to finding a solution than we'd been in months.

It's easy to get stuck in our own perspectives, or to be sure we've been wronged or offended by another person on purpose. We think that other person is terrible, mean, or stupid. We're mad, we have every right to be mad, and we're going to stay mad. When we practice generosity, we need to look at giving up our certainty that we are right.

We usually think of generosity in terms of material objects or time—instead of holding onto all of my money, I'm going to give some of it to someone else; instead of holding onto all of my time, I will donate some of it to help others. Generosity is also about letting go of our "damn certitude," as one of my friends calls it, and being willing to entertain the possibility that the other person's perspective has validity too. When we live from our giving hearts, we stop clinging to our convictions and open ourselves up to the other person's truth. That can change everything.

Just like our money or our time, our notions about ourselves, things, and other people are important to us. They help us navigate through life, make decisions, and move forward. When we bump up against another person, especially when there's conflict, our beliefs can really keep us from connecting with one another. We fall into patterns of "You always," "You never," or "I'm always the one who ends up saying I'm sorry, so I'm not going to do it this time." We hold our fixed ideas up like shields, but instead of protecting us, they just keep us apart.

Next time you find yourself in a conflict with someone, instead of rushing to the barricades, sure that you know the truth of the situation, think to yourself, "Maybe he has a point." By being willing to let go even that much, you can create an opening that will allow better understanding between you.

Share What You Have

Man should not consider his material possessions his own,
but common to all, so as to share them without
hesitation when others are in need.

—Saint Thomas Aquinas

I have a friend who, along with her sisters, inherited a summer cottage on a lake in Maine when their parents died. "It has been," she tells me ruefully, "quite an exercise in sharing. At first, it was used on a first-come, first-served basis. But then one of my sisters complained that she hardly ever used it while my other sister and I used it all the time, so she wanted first crack at the peak holiday times. Then there were the cleaning and repair issues: someone would break something and not replace it, and later there would be a tracking-down of the wrongdoer by a resentful sister forced to rectify the situation. I've been surprised at how difficult it's been and what feelings it stirs up."

As my friend discovered, sharing provides many opportunities to learn about ourselves and our capacity for generosity, possessiveness, self-righteousness, and cooperation. By sharing, we offer our resources to one another and are aided in return; we also treat the world more gently by avoiding the mindless accumulation of too many material things. Despite the insistence of well-crafted commercials, we do not need all the latest toys. One lawn mower can service many lawns; one cottage can shelter many families.

Most of us tend not to share as much as we can. My mother claims that whenever she borrows something she breaks it, so she doesn't want the burden of that on her head. I've tried sharing a camcorder with friends and have found this quite inconvenient. I can't just use it any time I want because I have to schedule it with them. I have happily shared my washer and dryer with my tenants for years, but I suppose that if they weren't naturally considerate, I would have to negotiate with them about when it was okay to traipse across my house with their clothes and run the very loud machines.

Sharing requires us to be in relationship with one another. We must negotiate the cottage schedule, or call and ask if we can borrow the VCR. If the sharing is unequal, we have to tread through all of our—and their—uncomfortable feelings.

In our world, sharing is important for two reasons. The Earth simply can't support everyone having everything they want. We must learn to share or we will destroy all life. It is also important that we allow ourselves opportunities to experience the feelings, good and bad, that sharing creates. It forces us to reach out and become less separate. When we choose to share something, we stretch our souls and spare the Earth—at least a little.

Become aware of your willingness or unwillingness to share by taking a few moments to go around your house and look at your things. Imagine that each of these things has a rubber band around it that is attached to you. For each item, notice how tight or loose the rubber band is. Which things are more closely attached to you? Which are looser? When I do this, I discover that the two things tightly attached to me are my hot tub and my photos. The rest of my "stuff" is much more loosely attached.

Pass It On to Your Kids

A seed will only become a flower if it gets sun and water.
—PSYCHIATRY PROFESSOR LOUIS GOTTSCHALK

I recently heard a story about how the Onondaga Indians used to teach their children about generosity. When it was time for someone to learn, the tribe would gather in a circle. The child would be brought into the center of the circle and given wonderful things to drink. After he had his fill, a voice would come from outside the circle saying, "I'm thirsty, I'm thirsty," and the child would be encouraged to take the drink to the thirsty person. The child would be brought back into the circle and fed fabulous food. After, he would hear a voice outside the circle saying, "I'm hungry, I'm hungry." Again, the child would leave the circle to feed the hungry person. The child would return to the circle and be given beautiful, warm clothes to wear. Again he would hear a voice crying, "I'm cold, I'm cold," and he would gather up clothes and help dress the freezing person.

Ever since contemporary social scientists have concluded that giving behavior is innate, they've become very interested in the study of altruism, asking why some people help while others don't, and which circumstances lead to help being offered. They have begun to study the childhoods of individuals who have demonstrated a high degree of altruism. The social scientists found that these folks had loving parents who instilled in them a healthy sense of self-esteem and self-efficacy. Their parents also instilled a strong sense of right and wrong as well; like the Onondaga Indians, altruists were taught specifically to be generous.

Most important, these folks had parents who modeled generosity. Studies of volunteers have also found that the majority of dedicated volunteers had parents who were also volunteers. Like any other aspect of parenting, we not only have to say what's right, we have to do what's right in order for our kids to learn. Instead of just telling them to be generous, we must demonstrate clearly and consistently our own generosity.

At Christmastime, I have always taken my stepkids, and now my daughter, to a toy store, where I let them pick out $100 worth of toys to give away to "Toys for Tots." They really got a kick out of thinking about the pleasure other kids would get from their selections. When I was a kid, we used to make up food baskets for families in need at Thanksgiving and go Christmas caroling at senior centers.

While these actions are wonderful, they only happen once a year, which isn't enough to instill the giving habit. My friend's grandmother used to do this simple practice with her: When you are doing something enjoyable with your child, like swimming, say something like, "We're having such fun. Let's take a minute to send this feeling of fun to all those kids who have never been in a pool." This way they'll learn, just as the Native American kids did, that giving comes from a sense of well-being, and that giving enhances the abundance that the giver is experiencing, rather than diminishing it.

Cultivate Spiritual Generosity

Regularly ask yourself, "How are my thoughts, words, and deeds affecting my friends, my spouse, my neighbor, my child, my employer, my subordinates, my fellow citizens? Am I doing my part to contribute to the spiritual progress of all I come into contact with?" Make it your business to draw out the best in others by being an exemplar yourself.

—Epictetus

Earlier in this section, I mentioned Jackie Waldman, the author of *The Courage to Give*. Jackie is one of the most remarkable people I have ever met in my life. Every time I speak with her, I hang up the phone committed to becoming more loving and generous. It's not that she lectures me on giving—far from it. Instead, she is such an example of the beauty and joy of selflessness that I am inspired to become the same.

All authors want their books to do well. Some want money, others want fame. Still others want to get their message across. While Jackie wants her message about the gifts of volunteerism to spread, she really wants her books to do well because of the people profiled in them. She has generously given a major portion of her royalties away to the charities associated with the people profiled, and if her book does well, they will prosper.

There are many different ways to be generous—monetarily, physically, emotionally, and yes, spiritually. Although we generally don't think about spiritual generosity, it is as real and important as any of the other forms. It is, as Epictetus points out, the offering of the essence of yourself to other people as a spiritual model, not because you've set yourself up on a pedestal to be adored, but because you've striven to live according to your values as much as possible. Gandhi, Mother Teresa, and Nelson Mandela are all examples of this kind of generosity. Through the power of their spiritual purity (which is not to say they didn't have faults or made mistakes), they had a huge impact on the fate of the world. If we think of their footsteps as a way of marking a path for us to walk along in our own way and at our own pace, their impact and their example become inspiring rather than daunting.

We don't have to try to liberate whole countries or heal lepers in order to cultivate our own unique brand of spiritual generosity. We only have to ask ourselves Epictetus' first question: How are my thoughts, words, and deeds affecting my friends, my spouse, my neighbors, my child, my employer, my subordinates, my fellow citizens?

This is plenty to work with for a lifetime, but here's